Books by Sidney Rosen

Galileo and the Magic Numbers

Doctor Paracelsus

Doctor Paracelsus

Illustrated by Rafaello Busoni

Doctor Paracelsus

by Sidney Rosen

Little, Brown and Company
Boston · Toronto

*The author wishes to thank Professor Robert Ulich of Harvard University
for his kind permission to use the song "Vacation Time." The song was translated from "Ferien" in* VAGANTENLIEDER (CARMINA BURANA), *Ulich &
Manitius, E. Diederichs, Jena, 1927.*

*Published simultaneously in Canada
by Little, Brown & Company (Canada) Limited*

PRINTED IN THE UNITED STATES OF AMERICA

To my mother and father, who would have enjoyed this book

Doctor Paracelsus

Chapter One

"THEO! WAKE UP, BOY!"

Theophrastus started up, staring about him with the dazed look of just waking. It was still night. He was in his little alcove bed, curtained off from the rest of his grandmother's bedchamber. Her hand was on his shoulder, still shaking him. In the other hand, she held a lighted taper high.

"Time to get up, Theo! Your father is already preparing for the journey."

At once, Theo remembered. It was the day of the great journey. Today he and his father were to leave the little Swiss village of Einsiedeln for the faraway land of Carinthia. Only the day before, Theo's father had drawn a crude map to show how their path would lead to the east, across the Alps, and then southward to the city of Villach.

"I have friends there," Theo's father had said. "We shall

begin a new life together, you and I. Remember all that I taught you about the different kinds of stones on the mountain?" Theo had nodded. "Well, at Villach there is a famous school where men go to learn the art of changing these stones into metals. I have been asked to teach there, for I know many secret ways to make rocks give up their metal hoards."

And Theo's heart had leaped with joy when his father had added, "On this journey, you shall have a horse of your very own."

Remembering all this in the blink of an eyelash, Theophrastus sprang from the bed. His grandmother set the candlestick on a small table next to the alcove. The little flame wavered, throwing uncertain shadows on the wall of the room.

Theo splashed water into his eyes from a small basin standing on the table.

"Better scrub well. The Lord only knows when you'll wash yourself clean again."

His grandmother removed her billowy white nightcap and began to comb her hair with long slow strokes. When she had finished, she opened the curtain of the closet where she kept her clothes and stepped inside.

Theo splashed a little more vigorously to show that he was paying attention. He rubbed his face and hands dry on a rough linen towel and began to put on the traveling clothes he had carefully laid out the night before. There was a pair of long brown hose that tied about his waist, a clean white shirt of linen, and a long-sleeved red doublet that was just a little too large and hung almost to his knees. He pulled short leather riding boots with peaked tops over his feet.

Meanwhile, his grandmother had reappeared, dressed in a

4

full pleated blue dress that reached to the floor. Over her head she deftly tied a great white hood that hung down to her shoulders. As she fastened a green sash about her waist, she kept muttering to herself.

"If you ask me, the whole thing is crazy. To drag a nine-year-old boy out of Switzerland a distance of three hundred miles! And for what? What will he find there that he cannot have at Einsiedeln? Wilhelm must be out of his head." Turning to Theophrastus, she said, "Come, your breakfast is ready downstairs."

An hour later, stuffed with eggs, milk, and dark peasant bread, Theophrastus stood by his father's side, helping with the last of the packing. Carefully, the little squat bottles filled with various herbs and decoctions were each wrapped in cloth and stowed away in the traveling packs.

Theo turned to his father. "Why does a doctor have to carry so many things with him?"

Wilhelm von Hohenheim smiled at his son. "These medicines are not easily acquired. It takes months, sometimes years, to find the proper herbs and animals. Then they must be prepared correctly to use in curing illness. A good physician never wastes a grain of medicine if he can help it."

"Someday, I shall become a great doctor like you, Father." Theo pointed to the bottles. "See, I've already learned many of the names: belladonna, vervain, friar's balsam."

"Well done, Theo." Doctor Wilhelm reached his hand down to tousle his son's hair. "On my word, you shall become a great doctor! A better one than myself, I am sure — and that will not take much doing." He sighed. "All doctors are said to be rich men. But I haven't been very successful here in Einsiedeln. We've been living almost like peasants — a fine comedown for members of a noble family! We have depended upon the kindness of your grandmother for our food and shelter. I imagine few people are convinced of my greatness."

"But you are a good doctor!" Theo sprang fiercely to his father's defense. "I've seen you make sick people well. And I've heard people say how kind you are, because you never ask for money from the poor."

"Well, now, let's not waste time talking about this." Wilhelm bent to his task again. "We must be packed and off with the sun. There's a long journey ahead of us."

6

"What is it like in Carinthia?"

"Well, the mountains are not as high as our Alps. But the hills are rich with silver, lead, and tin. You will see the lines where men dig for these treasures. The city of Villach itself is much larger than Einsiedeln. People there speak with a different accent, but you will be able to understand them."

Only a few more vials remained to be packed. "There, all is ready." The doctor tucked the last bottle away firmly. He closed the flap of the pack and tightened the leather strap that bound it. "Are you ready?"

Theo had been squatting beside the pack. Now he jumped to his feet, excitement burning in his eyes. "I've been ready since last night, Father."

"Let's find your grandmother. It's time to make our farewells."

At the gate of the inn, the horses were shaking their manes. Their forelegs struck against the ground with quick nervous movements, stamping away the stiffness of sleep. Doctor Wilhelm's horse was a brown gelding with a wise and experienced eye, a horse that could find his way home at night with the good doctor asleep in the saddle. Theophrastus sat astride a mottled gray filly, an alert, eager young horse, ready to find a bit of sugar or a sweet carrot in her master's pocket. A third horse, purchased especially for the occasion, carried the baggage.

"Good-by, Grandmother." Theophrastus bent in the saddle to hug his grandmother once more. She kissed him, and he saw that her eyes were full of tears. He wondered when he would see her again, and suddenly a lump seemed to form in his throat.

7

"God keep you both!" She examined Theo's cloak with a critical eye. "Are you warm enough?"

Theo pulled the heavy woolen garment about his shoulders and swallowed hard. "Have no fear, Grandmother."

"Don't forget to clean your ears when you wash!" She turned to her son-in-law. "Take care of him, Wilhelm."

"The boy will be all right, Mother Ochsner." The doctor bent over to kiss her cheek. "May God keep you well. Don't forget to take those pills I left, if you should have a weak spell."

She held his hand for a long moment. "You have been a good son-in-law, Wilhelm. If only Elsa had lived —"

"Time to go, Mother," said Wilhelm gently. He withdrew his hand and sat erect. The little black skullcap and the black robe that marked him as a physician gave his features a noble aspect. He motioned to Theo. Turning their horses, they clattered under the roof of the Devil's Bridge that spanned the leaping waters of the Sihl. Theo turned once to wave to Mother Ochsner. Another turn in the road and she was out of sight. Past the great tower of the Abbey of Einsiedeln, the road ran toward the mountain pass.

"Father!" called Theo as they trotted through a wide meadow. "Father, couldn't we stop here a moment?"

"Stop? What for?" But as Doctor Wilhelm's eyes followed Theo's outstretched hand, his face softened. "Yes, of course, Theo. We can stop for a moment." The boy had been pointing toward the little village cemetery next to the abbey. The two dismounted outside the gates, leaving the horses to crop the fine grass that grew there.

Man and boy paused before a small headstone that still bore the fresh marks of the stonemason's chisel. Theophrastus read the words to himself, stumbling a little over the syllables, for Wilhelm had begun to teach him Latin only a few months before.

REQUIESCAT IN PACE

ELSA OCHSNER VON HOHENHEIM

WIFE OF THE GOOD DOCTOR

WILHELM VON HOHENHEIM

d. 1502

They knelt on the grassy earth and said a prayer together. Theophrastus felt in an inner pocket of his robe and produced a small nosegay of wild flowers.

"I picked them yesterday, Father. Mother Ochsner kept them in water for me."

"That was a fine thing to do, son."

He is sensitive, thought Wilhelm, as he saw the tears well up in the boy's eyes. He will be a good doctor. Wilhelm put his arm about his son's shoulders and walked him slowly toward the gates.

Mounting again, the two turned their horses to the east, where the red fury of the sun had just begun to burn night away from the mountain's edge.

What a different world Villach was! Theophrastus had never seen so many houses of brick and wood all clustered together. The twisting, narrow streets were filled every moment of the day with people. There were husky miners dressed in rough leather jerkins, faces perpetually grimed from their work. Peasants crowded their way toward the market place, driving goats and donkeys before them. Wagons and carriages jolted over the cobblestone streets. Where Einsiedeln had been a world of quiet and rest, Villach was full of motion and excitement. Every day brought new sights, new wonders.

Once, Theo saw a knight, a real knight in armor, sitting proudly in his saddle on the back of a beautiful white horse. Behind him rode a valet-at-arms, carrying the knight's polished shield and long sharp lance. Theo forgot his manners and stared, mouth open, at this wonderful sight. Perhaps this was one of the very knights who, led by the Emperor Maximilian, had defeated the wicked Turks just outside of Villach only ten years before! All the exciting details of this great battle had been poured into Theo's ears by his father's friends.

Theophrastus and his father lived on the top floor of a small house on the outskirts of the city. From one window, Theo could see the steeples of the great Gothic church in the center of town and could get just a glimpse of the Drave

River beyond them as it flowed past Villach. From the other window, the steep cliffs of the mountain, the Villacher Alp, were visible, rearing themselves above the foothills where the mines lay.

As Wilhelm had told him, the heart and soul of Villach were the lead mines in the hills. Here men labored day and night to dig out the great veins of lead ore and to smelt out the pure metal. Most of the mines were owned by a very rich banker named Jacob Fugger. From Villach, Fugger sent his bars of pure lead all over the world to be sold or traded for other goods.

But changing the rough, lumpy metal ore into the smooth shiny metal was a difficult art which had to be taught to the workers. For this purpose, Jacob Fugger had built a school of mining in Villach. He had hired men skilled in the art of metallurgy to come from all over the world to teach in his school. Theo's father was one of these men. For, besides being a physician, Wilhelm had studied alchemy.

"Father, what is alchemy?" Theophrastus had asked, after hearing of his father's new position.

"It is an art, my son, which has to do with the secrets hidden by nature in all metals. The ancient peoples studied these secrets and knew them well."

"But what does an alchemist do?"

"It is difficult for me to explain it now, Theo. There are too many things you haven't learned yet. But in time —"

"What shall I have to know, Father?"

Wilhelm laughed. "Patience, patience! A good alchemist first learns the secrets of the stones."

"Will you help me learn those secrets?"

"Of course, if you want."

Theophrastus hopped up and down with joy. "I'll bring home different stones every day! And soon I shall be an alchemist and a doctor!"

"Not so loud. Remember there are neighbors living downstairs." But Theo's happiness was contagious. Forgetting his professional dignity, Wilhelm swept Theo high up into the air, tossed him, caught him again to the tune of joyous shrieks. One last swoop deposited Theo in a chair.

"And now for your reading lesson. How do you expect to become anything, if you remain an ignoramus?"

He placed the familiar Latin grammar under Theo's nose and pointed to a place on the open page. "Read."

Theo sighed. "Father, *must* I? I hate Latin! Why do we have to bother with this awful language?"

Wilhelm looked stern. "How many times must I tell you! Latin is the language of learned men, the language of physicians and scholars. Our everyday German is the language of peasants."

Theophrastus shrugged and resigned himself. Was it really worth all this to become like his father?

Every day, Theo went to the hillsides to find different kinds of rocks. He learned readily to recognize the dark fragments of lead-bearing rock called galena, and the yellowish stones that contained lead in another form. There were also reddish stones called bloodstones, which held iron inside them. Once he found a stone that gleamed like gold, and ran home in great excitement to show it to Wilhelm. But the physician told him that this rock merely contained iron in a secret form that resembled gold.

"This is a pyrite, or fool's gold, Theo. It is worthless, unless you are looking for iron ore. Learn to recognize it, so that its yellow gleam will not deceive you."

Further searches yielded bits of crystalline rock: agate, amethyst, quartz, and mica. Theophrastus soon knew the names of all the different kinds of mineral-bearing stones to be found near Villach.

But the exciting part of this new adventure was getting to know the miners. They were a rough lot, used to backbreaking labor. Yet even though their beards were unkempt and their clothes stiff with dirt, Theophrastus thought them the happiest men he had ever seen. They sang as they dug in the mines, as they hauled the ore from the pits, and as they strode down the hills at night to their crudely built wooden shacks in "miners' town" at the edge of the city.

Long tunnels had been pierced straight into the sides of the hills below the Villacher Alp. The entrances were shored up with heavy timbers to keep the roofs from collapsing. Into these long holes strode the miners each morning, picks and shovels over their shoulders. The lamps which they lit to see their way in the underground darkness swung at their belts. Above each tunnel, further up the side of the hill, were sunk a succession of vertical shafts. Wooden fans, cranked by boys, swept fresh air down some of these shafts into the mines.

Jacob Fugger was rich, and his mines were worked by the newest machines invented in the school of mines. The jagged chunks of galena were hauled up in huge buckets fastened to a long endless chain. At the top of a vertical shaft, the chain was wound around a wooden axle stuck through a cogwheel. Four horses, straining at leather harnesses, turned

13

a flat wheel with holes into which the cogs of the cogwheel fitted. As the horses went around, the buckets full of ore were drawn up and emptied into waiting carts by the workmen. Then the endless chain pulled the empty buckets, one after another, down into the mine tunnel. Horses drew the ore-filled carts down the log road to the smelting house.

And what magic went on there! The ore was heaped upon tables. Women, many of them miners' wives and daughters, separated pieces of ore from rock which contained no metal. Waste rock was tossed aside. Then the pounders, whose muscles bulged through their shirts damp with sweat, smashed the ore to bits with heavy flat hammers. These small pieces of galena were carried to the roasting ovens and mixed with secret ingredients known only to the master smelters. And out of the welter of flame and smoke, out of the billows of heat and soot, came the smooth gray flow of the liquid metal.

Theophrastus soon made friends with the miners. Not many boys in Villach showed such an interest in their work. Theo's curiosity pleased the men. Moreover, they knew that Theo's father never refused to treat any sick miner who came to him for help. And more likely than not, the good doctor didn't even mention a fee.

One afternoon, Theophrastus made his way slowly up the hillside, his eyes searching the ground for specimens of mineral rocks.

"Hello, boy!"

Theo looked up. It was Carl, one of the miners with whom he had struck up an acquaintance a week before. Carl was dressed almost completely in leather; both the jerkin over his shoulders and the wide apron tied about his middle were made of it. On his head was a peaked woolen cap with ear flaps that tied under the chin. In one hand, he carried a long single-bladed pick; in the other, he held a lamp.

"Carl! You're going to work late today."

"My wife was sick. But your father soon took care of that. He's a good man with medicine."

"He's the best physician in the world," said Theophrastus proudly.

"Aye, I'll take a bet on that." Carl looked at Theo slyly. "How'd you like to visit the mine for a little while today?"

The rocks spilled out of Theo's hands. "Oh, Carl, can I? Can I?"

Carl put down the lamp and scratched his head with a calloused finger. "It's a risky business. I'd be fired if the manager found out. Still, I know he's in the city today, and the fellows won't tell on me —" He paused. "Promise you'll do everything the way I say?"

"I promise, Carl. Cross my heart!"

Carl picked up the lamp and gave it to Theo. "All right, then. Up we go. And remember, mum's the word."

Shivering with anticipation, Theo followed Carl up to where the mine tunnel gaped like an open mouth.

The tunnel floor was smooth earth. It surprised Theo to find that by the time he and Carl had taken fifty paces, daylight had completely vanished. A small torch hung from a rafter, and Carl used this to light his lamp. In the flickering yellowish light, Theo could see that a framework of wooden beams supported the roof and sides of the tunnel about every ten feet.

"Be careful," warned Carl. The floor of the tunnel led to large steps cut in the dirt, going down.

"Where are the miners working?" asked Theophrastus. His words echoed faintly in the gloom of the mine.

"Two levels down. I can't take you there — too dangerous."

"But Carl —"

"Remember your promise?"

Theo was silent. Out of the corner of his eye Carl saw the boy's disappointed look. "Well, we'll go down one level, anyway," he said.

Theo heard a strange sound, a soft sighing that rose and fell. He pulled at Carl's jerkin. "What's that noise?"

"Noise?" Carl paused and listened. Then he laughed. "Just the fans, boy, blowing the clean air down here. We're coming to the first shaft. Here, look up now."

Theo saw the faint gleam of daylight high above and felt the rush of cool air on his cheek. "How deep are we now, Carl?"

Carl shrugged. "About fifty feet. See, this is where the lead ore was cut when the mine was opened." He held up the lamp so that Theophrastus could see the jagged face of the tunnel wall streaked with dark trickles of water. "No more galena here now — just hard rock."

Suddenly there were no more steps, just the smooth tunnel floor disappearing into the darkness ahead. "First level," said Carl. "Mostly worked out by now."

"I hear a funny noise," said Theo.

Carl stopped and listened again. "The pipes," he said.

"Pipes?"

"Sure, the pipes that pump out the water."

"Where does the water come from?"

16

Carl sighed. "All mines have water. At the lower levels it's always damp. The damp gets into your bones. It fills up a man's chest. Who knows? Maybe the evil gnomes send the water."

"Gnomes? What are gnomes?"

"They're the little men. Some people call them kobolds. They live inside the hills, and if they don't like the idea of your digging out the ore, then" — Carl made a slicing motion across his neck with one finger — "your goose is cooked!"

"Have you ever seen one?"

"I'm not sure. Down here, the dark plays tricks on a man's eyes. But I know plenty of miners who have. Hello, who's coming?"

A shadow moved out of the blackness and became a man. "That you, Carl?"

"George? Yes, it's me. How are things down there?"

"Miserable, as always. The air is bad, it's damp, and I swear I saw a kobold in the rock today. He jumped away and vanished in a puff of smoke, just as I swung my pick. Who is this with you?"

Carl held the lamp near Theo's face. "You know, Doctor von Hohenheim's boy. He wanted to see the inside of a mine."

George coughed. The sound echoed through the tunnel. "A bad business taking boys in here, Carl."

"I know." Carl touched Theo's arm. "Better go out with George now, Theo. I have to go down." Before Theo could protest, Carl reminded him. "Your promise?"

Theo nodded sadly. "Well, you got to see the mine, didn't you?" asked Carl.

Theo's face brightened. "Thank you, Carl." He followed

George back up toward the mine entrance. Every few moments, George had to stop to cough. At the mouth of the tunnel, George was seized with a coughing spell so violent he could hardly catch his breath. He finally spat phlegm into the dirt of the tunnel floor and leaned against a wooden beam, gasping.

The bright light of day made Theo blink. He thought that cough sounded serious. "Do you have a bad cold, George? My father will give you medicine."

George shook his head. "There's more than a cold in this old body, boy. It's the dust, boy, and the damp that get into a man's lungs and eat at them. No cure for it, boy. Just choke and cough, and hope you can live long enough to get out of the mines."

"When I am a doctor," said Theo, "I shall find a way to heal all the miners."

"Those are fine words to hear, boy. But most doctors can't be bothered with penniless miners."

"My father says that a doctor who won't cure a patient because he's poor is no doctor, but a thief."

George patted Theo's shoulder. "Your father's different, boy. He's our kind —"

Suddenly the ground quivered beneath their feet, and they heard a dull, far-off boom. George wheeled about and peered anxiously into the mine shaft.

"What was that?"

"Mercy of God, the fire damp!" George turned to Theo. "Run, boy! Run for your father, quick! Men's lives depend on how fast you can bring him. Hurry!"

Theo dashed down the hillside, his heart pounding. What

had happened down there in the blackness? As he ran, he heard the clang, clang of a hammer on ringing metal. It was the gong that was struck to signal an accident in the mines.

"What's wrong, boy?" people called as he ran toward the school. But Theo didn't stop to answer.

After his father had hurried away, there was nothing for him to do. He sat in the darkening room and peered through the window. On the hillside, he could now see more clearly the little flickers of the lamps moving in a kind of figured dance, as men swarmed about the mine shaft. What had happened down there? His father had forbidden him to return to the mine.

Was it the gnome George had seen? What sort of dangers and poisons were in the mines that blew men up in flames, suffocated them silently, and tore away their lungs?

Someday, when I am the greatest doctor in the world, I

shall find out, Theo promised himself. I shall take care of the miners and heal all their sickness.

He heard his father's step on the stairs and rushed to blow up the fire, which had died to a glow on the hearth. Then he used a bit of kindling to light the candles. When Wilhelm entered, Theo could see that his face was sad. Something terrible had happened.

"The mine, Father, what happened?"

"It was the fire damp, Theo. An explosion. Very bad — I don't want to talk about it."

"I am not afraid, Father."

Wilhelm put his arm about Theo. "I know that, son. But I have seen much death and dying this afternoon, and I am tired."

"Father, do you know the miner named Carl?"

"There are many miners named Carl."

"His wife was sick this morning."

"Oh, you mean Carl Dienst. Well?"

"Was he — was he —"

"He was helping carry out the injured."

Theo sighed with relief. "Thank the Lord!"

Wilhelm looked at him questioningly. Theo knew he had to tell his father the truth. "I was in that mine, Father. Just before the explosion. But it wasn't Carl's fault. I made him take me." And he told how Carl had kept him away from the dangerous level of the mine.

"Promise me you won't go near the mines again." Theo signed a cross over his heart with one finger. "Poor Carl," added Wilhelm, "he's probably feeling pangs of guilt about it right now. He thought that being good to you was a way of repaying my treatment of his wife. Theo, I ought to give you a good spanking!"

Theo sighed with relief. It had been such an exciting adventure. He reminded himself to tell Wilhelm about his plan to cure all miners of their sicknesses when he grew up.

As the days passed, Theo missed his walks up the hillside to the mines. He began to beg his father for permission to visit the alchemist of the Fugger school of mines. Doctor Wilhelm finally agreed to such a visit.

"I spoke to Johann Schwinger, the chief alchemist, about you. He says you may come."

Into Theo's eyes came the spark that Wilhelm had learned to recognize. "All right, all right. Don't jump. Remain calm. Remember, he is a busy man, with many things to do. You will stay in a corner and watch, without disturbing him."

Theo choked down his excitement until his father had left the room. Then he could no longer hold in his bottled-up feelings. With an ecstatic whoop that could almost be heard back in Einsiedeln, he exploded into the air like an uncoiling spring. He was going to meet a real alchemist! He was going to see a man at work discovering the untold secrets of nature!

Johann Schwinger was small and gnomelike, almost fitting the description of the little kobolds who lived in the black recesses of the mines.

"What is your name, boy? Your full name, and no nonsense about it."

Theo was a little frightened by this directness. He stammered a little. "Phi — Phi — Phillip Theophrastus Bombast von Hohenheim, sir."

"Too big a mouthful. What do they call you for short?"

"Theo, sir."

"Theo it is, then."

Wilhelm had been looking on with amusement. "I have told the boy not to bother you, Johann. If he becomes annoying, send him out at once."

"Bother? What bother?" cried Johann. He wore a dirty, stained leather apron about his waist, and Theo could see that his hands were crisscrossed by the lines of old scars. Johann had a habit of shuffling back and forth nervously as he talked. "What is all this nonsense about bother? There are all too few among our youth who are interested in the secret arts. If your boy is really interested in alchemy, why then, he's welcome. Come along." His stained fingers tugged at Theo's elbow.

He led Theo down a narrow staircase that spiraled into the deep cellars of the school building. Here, the way had to be lighted by great tallow lamps set into niches in the stone walls.

"Watch your step, boy." Johann chuckled. "If you want to become a good alchemist, you'll have to get used to cellars. Don't know why, but we always seem to end down at the bottom of everything." He stopped at the end of a short corridor and flung open a stout, metal-barred door. "Well, here is my laboratory. Come in, Theo, come in."

What a wealth of things to be seen, once his eyes became used to the gloom! There was a great barrel-shaped furnace in one corner, with a hood of copper rising up to the ceiling. Into the back of the furnace was fixed the mouth of a big leather bellows, to blow up the fire. And everywhere, on the tables, on the shelves, in the corners, were vessels of all shapes and sizes. Some were fat, some thin, some squeezed thin in the middle. Some had handles, some long spouts, and some had strange twisted pipes coming from them. There were glass vessels and iron ones, pewter and earthenware.

On one table stood mortars and pestles for grinding powders. On another stood a large balance for weighing. Along the walls were shelves from floor to ceiling. These were crowded with bottles filled with strangely colored liquids, white powders, black powders, herbs, stones, and bits of metals. And everywhere, on the shelves, in odd corners, on the tables, on chairs, in helter-skelter profusion were hundreds of books and manuscripts.

There was an odd smell in the room, a smell of smoke and soot mixed with a touch of exotic sweet aromas. On the furnace stood a great iron bottle. From its top, a twisted spiral pipe ran into the mouth of a clear glass jar with a long, swan-like neck. Johann hurried to the furnace and peered into the jar.

"Aha! The essence has gone over! So far, all is well."

Theo, remembering his father's warning, said nothing.

"Well, Theo, cat got your tongue? Don't you want to know what I'm doing?"

Theo blinked in surprise. "Yes, sir, I do!"

"Well, look here now. I am preparing a pure tincture." Johann pointed to the long-necked glass jar.

Theo suddenly recalled something his father had told him about alchemy. "Are you making gold, sir?"

Johann threw back his head and roared with laughter. "Gold? No, boy, I have no time to fool with gold! I am only searching for ways to refine metals into purer states. But there was a time when I spent many fruitless years trying to find the transmuter of all metals."

"Trans — trans-mu-ter? What's that, sir?"

The alchemist waggled a long forefinger under Theo's nose. "Now look here, boy, if we are to get along, then it's 'Johann,' not 'sir.' Understand?"

"Yes, s — Johann."

"Better. Has your father ever told you of the philosophers' stone?" Theo shook his head. "Now that is the greatest mystery for which most alchemists search. That is the great magisterium which changes all base metals, like lead or quicksilver, into pure gold or silver. What is more, the stone has the power to give everlasting life to him who drinks a potion containing it. And it can cure any sickness."

"Did you ever find it, Johann?"

A dreamy look veiled the little alchemist's eyes. "Ah, once, many years ago, I came close. Oh, so close, boy, so close!" He held up the thumb and forefinger of one hand. "It was up north, in the city of Prague. There, in a little bookshop on a side street, I discovered a manuscript written in a strange language. But I recognized the symbols. Why, as I remember, I still have it here somewhere."

He began to search among the piles of books and manuscripts, flinging them heedlessly to the floor, until he held up a stained, dog-eared piece of parchment. "Look here, boy!" He unrolled it before Theo's wide eyes and pointed to a series of symbols printed on the parchment.

"See that? This is part of the secret formulas of the ancient Egyptian master alchemist, Hermes Trismegistos, the greatest of them all. These symbols were discovered engraved

on pure emerald tablets held in the hands of his mummified
body. And when I found this manuscript, I knew I had it
— the secret of the stone!"

"What did you do then?"

"First, I told no one." Johann's eyes had a sly look. "That
is an important lesson for an alchemist to learn — how to
keep a secret."

"But why, Johann?"

"Why? Oh, it is easy to see that you are very young. Because, Theo, there are men in this world so greedy they would
do anything for a gold ducat. And when such men are in
power, when they are kings, or dukes, or princes, they are
always on the watch for ways to get more gold. When they
discover some poor wretch who brags that he has the secret

of the stone, they feed him with lies and flattery. When he suspects the least, they torture him to get the formula. Oh, I tell you, an alchemist's life is worth little these days, unless he can keep a secret."

Johann pointed again to the parchment, his fingers under a line of strange symbols:

"You see, that is the way to begin. First the pure philosophic Sulfur and Mercury must be coaxed out of the impure bodies which —" Johann stopped suddenly, one hand clapped to his forehead. "What a dunderhead I am! Here I chatter on and on as though you were a fellow practitioner of the art. And you haven't understood one word of what I have said, have you?"

Theo shook his head. "But I want to know, Johann! Will you teach me?"

"And why do you think I asked you here in the first place? I can tell a budding alchemist when I see one, boy. Now then, for a beginning. As we have been taught by Aristotle, all substances are composed of combinations of four basic elements. These are —"

"I know, Johann," interrupted Theo eagerly. "Fire, the lightest, Air, Water, and Earth, the heaviest!"

"Good! Then it will not be hard for you to understand. Now then, the problem is, how can one substance be changed into another? And the answer is, by means of the qualities which those substances have in common. Look here —" Johann found a piece of charcoal and began to scrawl a diagram on the back of an old manuscript. As he drew, he kept talking.

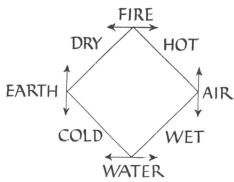

"Each element possesses two different qualities. Each of these qualities is shared with other elements. Look, suppose I burn a piece of wood. That means Earth changes into Fire. How does that happen? Well, Fire is hot and dry and Earth is cold and dry. They can be interchanged by virtue of the common quality of dryness."

"I see how it is!" cried Theo. "Then boiling water becomes invisible Air, because Water and Air share the quality of wetness."

"Good, good! You learn quickly, boy. It is the alchemist, you see, who must search out these qualities in substances, in order to discover how one may be transmuted into another."

"But, Johann, this is like magic!"

Johann waved his hand. "Magic? Nonsense! There is no abracadabra here, boy. This is nature itself. God has made the universe in a very wonderful and mysterious way, and

27

man may share in some of its secrets. The clues to their discovery are all about us, in the stars, in the positions of the planets, in the ways that metals are hidden in the earth. The alchemist must search out all these clues. Then, by practicing the art of alchemy in his laboratory, he will discover those secrets of nature that God has meant man to discover."

Theo picked up the old parchment and gazed eagerly at the symbols printed on it. "Oh, Johann, will I ever understand all this?"

Johann's intense gaze softened to a smile. "I'm sure you will, Theo, if you want to." He cleared his throat. "Well now, let's have a look at what has been on the fire."

He strode to the furnace. Using a thick cloth to protect his hand, he picked up the long-necked flask gingerly. "This vessel is a retort. And in here is some distilled essence of Luna. That means silver. Now, I add to this some salt of Mars —" He put the retort on a table and poured a white crystalline powder from a vial into the clear liquid. There was a hissing, and the mixture suddenly sparkled red.

Gazing intently into the bubbling, crimson contents of the vessel, Theo silently vowed to spend the rest of his life searching out the mysteries God had hidden in nature.

Chapter Two

THEO, IT IS TIME FOR US TO HAVE A TALK."
Doctor Wilhelm paced slowly to and fro before his
son, who was seated on a small stool. The doctor wore
a loose, comfortable lounging robe of black cloth trimmed
with red velvet. Theo was dressed for sleeping. It was late;
as he listened to his father, he sipped slowly a cup of warm
milk. Bright flames crackled in the fireplace. The room was
warm and filled with familiar smells: birch smoke, roast meat,
and the sharp tang of medicinal herbs.

"We must begin to think about your future."

Theo swallowed a gulp of milk. "But, Father, you know I
want to be a physician and an alchemist, like you!"

"Are you sure this is what you want?" Theo nodded vigorously. The doctor smiled. "Then I'm glad. I've always
dreamed that you might follow in my footsteps; better still,
that you would surpass me in wealth and in deeds." His face

became serious again. "But it is a difficult matter, Theo. You know that while we do not lack for the necessities of life, I am not a rich man. Still, I have thought of a way to begin your education."

"Can't you and Johann teach me all I have to know?" Theo licked the last drop of milk from the rim and set the cup on the floor.

Wilhelm laughed. "No, no! I know that Johann has taught you some of the secrets of alchemy. And I have managed to beat a little Latin into your head. But to become a physician, you must learn much, much more. In the first place, you must learn Latin well enough to speak it fluently."

"Speak it?" Theo sounded disgusted. "I can read Latin. Isn't that enough?"

"Hardly. At the university, you will be expected to listen to lectures delivered in Latin, to write notes in Latin, and to defend your thesis in Latin."

"Thesis? What's a thesis, Father?"

"Let me see if I can explain." Doctor Wilhelm paused a moment in thought, the long fingers of one hand touching his brow. "After you have studied all your subjects and have passed all your examinations, you must receive your degree. This means that the faculty of the university accept you into their company as a scholar. But first, you must prove to them that you can stand on your own two feet and exhibit the ability to argue intelligently on any subject. So you select a thesis, some statement which you will either defend or argue against."

"What kind of statement?"

Wilhelm scratched his head. "Well, let us take this statement from the books of the great doctor Galen: pus in a wound is necessary for healing. You announce that you will defend this thesis. Then all the professors and students come on a certain day to argue against you. They may try all kinds of tricks in logic to knock your thesis down. If you defend yourself well, you earn your degree and you graduate from the university."

"Whew!" cried Theo. "What a fearful business that must be!" Then, seeing the smile on his father's face, he added, "I would still rather learn from you and Johann."

"Nevertheless, I have arranged for you to leave next month for the monastery school at Lavanttal. There you will receive the training you need in order to be eligible for the university. The headmaster is a friend of mine — Bishop Erhardt. I hope he finds you as good a pupil as does Johann."

And indeed, Johann had found Theo to be a very apt pupil. It seemed as though Theo could never learn enough about the secrets that nature had stored in metals.

Theo had learned all the mystic symbols and images used by alchemists to describe their experiments. Since no alchemist trusted any other alchemist, each had his own set of mysterious symbols representing the different metals and the ways they were changed into other substances by alchemy. For example, the metal gold was often represented by the image of the sun, but just as often as a red king.

One day Johann told him something Theo found difficult to understand. "All the stuff of the earth," said Johann, "is simply made up of two primary substances: Sulfur and Mercury."

Theo looked puzzled. "But Johann, isn't sulfur just that

31

yellow stuff that burns and gives off a bad smell? Father uses it once in a while, I know."

"Let us do an experiment." Johann hunted through the shelves, finally taking down a jar filled with a blackish powder. He poured a little of this on a stone slab and placed the slab in the great furnace.

"You will notice that when matter burns, part of it disappears." Johann ignited the powder, which began to burn with a furious red flame. "Now tell me, Theo, with which of the four elements of Aristotle do you connect this burning?"

"With Fire, of course," said Theo quickly, "hot and dry."

"Correct. Now then, Sulfur represents the principle of burning that is in all things. This is different from the *material* sulfur you were talking about, which is called brimstone."

"I don't understand the difference."

"I'll try to explain." Johann pointed to the flames. "There is no *material* sulfur in that powder. The material things in this world are the things we touch and feel and smell and see. But there are also things which are beyond our senses — the spirits, the souls which are inside the material things. When I use the word sulfur to describe one of the elements, I am talking about one of the two souls that can be inside real matter. Alchemists call this the *sophic* Sulfur."

"Sophic?"

Johann chuckled. "Short for *philosophic.*"

Theo looked about the laboratory. Could it be that these staunch brick walls, these very coals in the furnace, the grains of powder now being consumed in flame — could it be that they were all alive? Did there exist somewhere inside them a spirit that came to life under the skillful hands of the alchemist? Theo stared at the flame in a muse, and it seemed to him that in the little flickering tongues of red and yellow he could see a form of life, something alive dancing there . . .

Johann's sharp voice snapped him back to reality. "Now then, to continue. The sophic Mercury is the soul inside all metals. This Mercury is also quite different from the *material* mercury we call quicksilver. But the sophic Mercury has the elemental qualities of the material substance — cold and wet."

"Oh," interrupted Theo, "that's the element Water."

"Right you are!"

"But," pointed out Theo with growing excitement, "Water puts out Fire. Then Sulfur and Mercury are opposite to each other and cannot mix!"

"Yes," said Johann, "and that's exactly what the ancient philosophers believed. But this is the year 1504; these are modern times! We have learned much since the old days. You see, about seven hundred years ago, a great alchemical master who lived in the Moslem world discovered that the two elements could mix. His name was Geber. He found a red stone that would give both quicksilver and sulfur when heated properly."

Theo sighed. "Oh, there is so much to know about the world, Johann. Will I ever learn it all?"

"I don't think any one man will ever learn it all." Johann's eyes looked deep into Theo's. "But I think that someday you will know far more about nature than I can ever tell you."

He shook his head and punched a long forefinger playfully into Theo's ribs. "Hey, there, remember what I told you? An alchemist's fire must never go out. Look alive, boy. How about

33

fetching some coal for that furnace? Remember, you are going to help me with my next experiment."

Theo leaped to the hook in the wall where his leather apron hung. He knotted the thongs about his waist with anxious fingers. As he began to toss coals from the bin into the coal scuttle, he thought: At last I am becoming a real alchemist!

"So you are Wilhelm's boy. Welcome to Lavanttal!"

The man who spoke was tall and somewhat portly. He wore a white robe that fell in folds to his ankles and was tied with a rope sash. A few silver hairs strayed from under the white skullcap on his head. On one finger of the hand he held out to Theo was a large gold ring with a deep red ruby set in its center.

"Thank you, sir."

So this was the famous Bishop Erhardt of the Lavanttal monastery school. Why, he didn't look like a schoolmaster at all! Theo saw only kindness in the bishop's face and a twinkle in his eyes. He took the bishop's hand and kissed it with the proper reverence.

"Well, sit down, my lad. You've had a long day's journey." Bishop Erhardt motioned Theo to a high, straight-backed chair. "Have you been assigned a bed in the dormitory?"

"Yes, sir."

Theo had already heard, from the pupil who had shown him his bed, about the rigors of student life at Lavanttal. The bed was simply a wooden frame on which was a straw-stuffed sack covered with one blanket. "Up at five every morning," the boy had whispered in Theo's ear, for prayers and a breakfast of gruel, milk, and bread. Then classes until noon. A

simple lunch of cheese and bread, and then an hour for meditation. Classes again until six. Supper and evening prayers.
Study hours until nine, when all lights were out. And, the boy
had added, at Lavanttal, one had better know one's lessons
well. Theo's hose and jerkin would be taken away from him; he
would not see them again until the day he left. He would be
given a long brown robe of coarse material, with a rope belt
and a hood that covered the head. The new clothing looked
strange; probably it itched. As he faced Bishop Erhardt in
the headmaster's rooms, Theo was not sure he was going to
like Lavanttal.

"Good, good! You know our routine, of course. Our life is
simple here, and we are dedicated to learning. You will study
Latin and Greek in preparation for the university."

Theo could not help himself; he made a wry face. The bishop's eyebrows went up. "Upon my word, why such a horrid expression?"

Theo was ashamed. He kept his eyes fixed on the ground. "I'm sorry, sir. It's just that I'm not very fond of Latin, sir."

"And what are you fond of?"

"Alchemy, sir."

The bishop's eyebrows went up even higher. "Alchemy? But what can you —" He stopped and motioned for Theo to rise. "Come with me, lad." He opened a door and waved Theo across the threshold. Theo took two steps and gasped with surprise. The room was an alchemical laboratory, completely outfitted from bottles to furnace!

The bishop pointed to a great flask with two necks. "Know what that is, lad?"

"A pelican, sir."

"That's right. And this vessel?"

"A retort, sir."

"And this?"

"A crucible, sir."

Bishop Erhardt looked surprised. "Not bad for a twelve-year-old fledgling. But let us see further." He thrust a piece of parchment and a pen into Theo's hands. "Can you possibly write down the names of the seven metals, lad?"

Theo smiled. He knew he could recite the list of metals backwards, standing on his head! He began to write the names, drawing the symbol for each metal under the name.

Gold. The Sun.

Silver. The Moon.

Iron. Mars.

Quicksilver. Mercury.

Tin. Jupiter.

Lead. Saturn.

Copper. Venus.

Bishop Erhardt took the parchment and scanned it carefully. "Well done, my boy! I see that you also know all the planets that go with the metals. Where did you learn this?"

And as the bishop listened, Theo told him of the days spent in Johann's laboratory at the Fugger school of mines. The bishop nodded understandingly. "And you'd rather be back there with Johann than studying Latin up here, eh?"

"I — I didn't say that, sir."

A crafty look came into the bishop's eye. He slapped his hand upon a table. "I'll tell you what, young Master von Hohenheim, I'll make a bargain with you. If you can stick to the Latin and Greek studies here, and do well, we shall spend one afternoon a week in my laboratory. A bargain?"

Theo's eyes flashed. "Oh, yes, sir!"

"Let's have your hand on it, then. And now, off with you! It's almost time for lunch and afternoon classes."

The monastery school was remote from the city. Life there seemed to be a steadily flowing stream that moved so swiftly one scarcely noted the passing of time. The weeks and the months sped by for Theo. Much more attention was paid to Latin than to Greek. The lessons from the stained, well-worn Donatus Latin grammar were all learned by heart. Theo read the orations of Cato and Cicero, and fumbled his way through the poetry of Ovid and Virgil. Little by little, Latin became easier to read and write. Slowly, he moved from the first Latin phrases spoken in a stumbling fashion to long sentences glibly recited.

But one thing made all the hours spent on Latin worth while — the weekly afternoons in the laboratory. There the learned bishop gave Theo a closer look at the wonders of alchemy.

The old man and the boy would sit at one of the laboratory tables and talk, and time would be forgotten.

"But, sir, what do the planets have to do with the seven metals?"

"Wise men know, Theo, that the planets moving in the sky control more than the destiny of mankind. The planets wield their power over all the events in the world." The bishop pointed to the shelves crammed with bottles. "That includes the making of different kinds of matter. Astrology is the science which links the motions of the stars and the planets to all the happenings in the world. That is why an alchemist must learn his astrology thoroughly."

"How does an alchemist use astrology?"

"Why, sometimes an entire experiment can be ruined because the *time* for it was ill-chosen. You must learn the times when the planets are in conjunction and when they are in opposition."

Theo shook his head. "I don't know what that means."

The bishop waved his hand. "Don't grieve about it so, Theo. You will learn all about such things at the university, when you study astronomy. I was merely talking about the times when the planets are lined up on the same side of the earth, or when they are lined up on opposite sides of the earth. The time will soon come when you will be ready for such studies."

Bishop Erhardt was right. Quickly, Theo's stay at Lavanttal came to an end. It was difficult to believe that two whole years had gone by. Theo was no longer afraid of Latin. He could converse in the language as well as any other boy in his class. But he hated to bid the good bishop farewell.

39

"I expect to hear great things about you, Theo. Write to me once in a while. May the blessings of God go with you."

And then Theo sat once again on the small stool in his father's study. The flames glinted red and yellow in the fireplace, and all the old familiar smells were there.

"You're old enough for the university, son. After all, at fourteen one is already a man! So, it is decided. I have sent your first year's tuition on to the University of Tübingen. That's where I studied, you know. Classes begin in about two weeks, so you'll have to start out at once." A worried look appeared on Doctor Wilhelm's face.

"What is it, Father?"

"Well, I had planned to travel with you, but I can't get away. Perhaps one of the miners will go along — I'll ask Carl."

Theo rose. "Why can't I go alone, Father?"

"On such a long journey? You know how dangerous the road is these days. There are robbers and mountebanks. There are scoundrels who would just as soon cut your throat as look at you. Wouldn't you be afraid?"

Theo squared his shoulders and looked straight at his father. "Afraid? Why, they are only people, human beings like myself! Why should I fear them? I can take care of myself, Father. Let me go alone."

Doctor Wilhelm looked at his son for a long moment. He saw the short figure, the round head a little too large for the body, the serious face already looking too old, the strength and certainty in the eyes. The physician shrugged his shoulders. "Alone? Yes, why not! At fourteen, I was on my own already. Of course you may go alone, if you wish."

40

"Thank you, Father!" Theo's eyes were on the future. The university and the whole world of knowledge lay before him!

As Theo turned his mare onto the road that led down into the valley of the Neckar River, he could see the roofs of Tübingen below him. There were the stone walls and watch-towers of the castle and the spire of the church. And there, as his father had described, were the university buildings, formed into a quadrangle and surrounded by a great wall. The city houses were like those of Villach, high, with small, many-paned windows and steeply slanting roofs.

It was early morning. The road led into the central market place of the town, and Theo passed the wagons of farmers carrying produce to be sold. The farmers all seemed to dress alike. They wore shirts of homespun under leather jerkins, and short breeches over brown hose. On their feet were heavy leather boots; their heads were covered by large, flat, brimmed hats, greasy and stained with wear. The men puffed at curved pipes and shouted coarse jokes. As Theo rode past, many doffed their hats and called out "Good morning!"

At the university, Theo found himself in the midst of a hubbub. The courtyard was filled with first-year students who had come to register. Mingled with them were upperclassmen who had come to meet entering students who were family friends, or who just wanted to see what the new crop was like.

Theo had left his horse at a nearby livery stable, and now found himself in the long registration line. He tried to listen to what other students were saying. Suddenly he realized that many were speaking strange tongues. There were boys here from all over Europe, and the air was filled with phrases in German, Latin, French, Italian, English, and Spanish.

"Hey, what nationality are you?"

Theo turned. The youth behind him in the line had spoken. "I'm Swiss. And you?"

"German. From Salzburg. What a business, this waiting in line! It's worse than the army."

"You're right." Theo had no idea of what the army was like, but this fellow sounded very sophisticated. Theo didn't want to appear a country bumpkin.

"My name is Hans Ziller. What's yours?"

"Theophrastus von Hohenheim. But my friends call me Theo."

"Von Hohenheim, eh?" Hans had a doubtful look in his eye. "A noble family."

Theo looked at Hans in an equally critical way. Ziller's clothes were far handsomer than his own. That velvet doublet alone must have been worth many guilders.

Hans caught Theo's eye and laughed. "Don't let these fancy clothes fool you. They're a present from the baron for whom my father farms. I had a chance to go to the monastery school, and the abbot there managed to persuade the baron to send me to the university. But clothes do make the man. You would never guess that here stands Hans Ziller, son of a German serf."

Theo smiled. "My title isn't worth much in cash. And my father is just a poor country physician — a good one, mind you, but not a very rich one."

Hans clapped Theo on the back. "Von Hohenheim, I like you! Let's be friends. How about rooming with me? I hear it's cheaper for two students to live together."

"Agreed!" The two new friends shook hands warmly.

"What are you going to study?" asked Hans, as they edged forward toward the registration office.

"Medicine. I'm going to be a doctor, just like my father. You, also?"

Hans shook his head and made a wry face. "Ooof! No, I can't stand the smell of medicine. I'm going to study law and become rich. I've had my taste of being a peasant."

"Rich or poor," said Theo firmly, "I just want to be a good doctor."

They had reached the registration office. There were papers to sign and documents to fill out. The university officials all spoke Latin. They all appeared to be stern men who would brook no nonsense. After the papers had been signed, the freshmen were led to the great lecture hall, the Aula Magna of the university.

A robed man standing by a side door rapped on the floor three times with a wooden staff and commanded the students to rise. The door opened and the Rector of the University walked in. He wore a magnificent robe of black velvet, trimmed with ermine, and topped with a crimson hood. On his head was the traditional square cap of the doctor of philosophy, rising to a small point in the center. The rector strode to the center of the rostrum, where a great Bible had been placed on a table.

He faced the students and, speaking in precise Latin, explained the rules of the university. Theo learned that he would have to wear a black gown and cap to all classes, and nod and tip his hat if he met a professor or university official. Boisterous conduct was not permitted. Notes had to be taken at lectures, and these notes would be examined once a month by the professors. A student who was caught selling his books in order to purchase wine or other foolish luxuries would be expelled at once.

"And now, gentlemen," declared the rector, pointing to the Bible, "you are about to swear the oaths of obedience. Let me remind you of the terrible penalties of perjury, should you feel inclined to break one of these oaths. Please raise your right hands and repeat after me: *I swear that I will attend all lectures faithfully. I swear that I will not cheat during examinations. I swear that I will show obedience to every officer of this University. I swear that I will not willfully kill or injure a professor who fails me in a subject. I swear —*"

The oath-taking proceeded for a good ten minutes. By the time the last oath had been sworn, Theo scarcely remembered the first. Finally, the freshmen were dismissed.

Hans suggested that they find a room.

"By all means. Only, where shall we begin?"

Hans scratched his ear and looked puzzled. "Tübingen is one town I know nothing about. Let's ask that upperclassman over there." They approached a black-gowned student, who lolled against a post and favored them with a supercilious smile.

"A room? Have you fledglings dared leave your mothers' nests?"

Theo reddened, and his hands curled up into fists. "My mother is dead!" he muttered, taking a step forward.

"No offense! No offense!" The upperclassman stepped back hastily. "I admit it was a bad joke. Look here, you fellows might try Frau Mueller's rooming house on Straw Street. It's not a knight's parlor, but it's comfortable and cheap."

"Cheap? That's for us!" cried Hans. "Straw Street? That's a queer name."

"Oh, that's the nickname for the street called Alterstrasse. You see, when the great University of Paris was founded, the students and professors were mostly poor members of the clergy. All the classes were held in houses along one street. The benches in the rooms were just bundles of straw. Even the professors sat on straw to keep them from the cold floor. And this street was called Straw Street. Now there's a Straw Street in almost every university town in Europe."

"Thanks for the tip, friend," said Hans. "Off to Straw Street!" Taking Theo's arm, he marched him off, whistling a soldier's tune between his teeth. Theo decided he liked his boisterous new friend. Suddenly he remembered.

"My horse! She's stabled just around this corner."

"Horse?" asked Hans. "What will you want with a horse in Tübingen? Have you so much money, you can afford to stable a horse?"

Wistfully, Theo shook his head. The mare would have to be sold. The transaction did not take long. With Hans, who prided himself on a knowledge of horses, bargaining all the way, the mare fetched fifty crowns from the grumbling stable-keeper. Theo poured the gold coins into his purse, which bulged so, the drawstrings would not close. Then, with light step, they headed for Straw Street.

Frau Mueller was a thin little woman with a long, sad face. She was dressed in black from head to foot.

"I'm still mourning for my husband, God rest his soul," she whined, "dead these five years and no better man to replace him."

Later, Hans and Theo discovered that this was a pose calculated to soften the tax collector's heart. The students in her house called her "The Black Widow." But she had a good heart. More than once, she slipped a bit of supper to a penniless student who had not eaten all day. And while she might hint and complain about overdue rent, no student had ever been dismissed from her door for that reason.

Frau Mueller showed them a large, sunny room, with two beds and two desks. A moment later, Hans and Theo pressed some coins into her hand and they had their room. They slung their packs down on the beds and looked at each other.

"Well," said Hans, "as it says in the marriage ceremony: for better or for worse!"

Theo felt a sudden gnawing in his stomach. "Hans! We haven't had our dinner yet. I'm starving!"

"Let's go. There must be a tavern nearby where we can dine cheaply."

The tavern was a small, badly lit room smelling of beer and soot. At one end was a huge brick fireplace filled with a bed of glowing coals. Over this, stuck on a long iron spit, were dripping joints of roasting meat. A small boy, so smeared with soot and grime that he seemed to be part of the fireplace, turned the crank which kept the meat rotating over the coals. As the fat and juices dripped off the meat, little yellow flames flared up with a hiss.

Next to the fireplace, on a platform, were two great kegs with wooden spouts stuck into them. The rest of the room was filled with crude tables and benches. Two plump, rosy waitresses hurried between the tables and the beer kegs, carrying away empty mugs and bringing filled ones. At the

tables sat groups of students and townspeople, eating, drinking, and singing. Theo and Hans found places at one of the student tables and ordered meat and drink.

"Well, this seems to be a jolly place," said Hans, pointing to another group of students, who were bellowing one of the university songs. Next to them sat some serious workingmen watching two of their group play a game of dominoes. One of the fat waitresses slapped platters of meat before Hans and Theo. Taking out their knives, they began to eat heartily.

One moment, the two friends were eating peacefully; the next, pandemonium had broken loose in the tavern. There was a drunken laugh, an indignant cry, and the crash of an overturning table. One of the students had prankishly interfered in the domino game. The player, whose pieces had been disturbed, had struck the student in the face. And now, in an ominous quiet, the men in the room stood face to face in two groups — the city men and the students. The waitresses and

47

the grimy boy had disappeared. Involuntarily, Theo and Hans, knives still in their hands, found themselves standing with the students. More knives appeared in hands. The townspeople seized long wooden staffs that had been stacked in a corner. Some of these staffs had sharp iron points attached.

One of the city men stepped forward and spat on the floor. "Death to all student-pigs who dirty the streets of Tübingen!" he cried.

The students looked at each other. They were only twelve in number, facing more than twenty armed, menacing towns-people. One black-gowned boy spun about, flung the door open, and shouted into the night, "Riot! Riot! All students, here! Riot!"

At the same moment, one of the opposite group flung open one of the small windows of the tavern and screamed, "Men of Tübingen! To the Red Donkey! Riot! Riot!"

Theo gulped. He remembered now the stories his father had told him of the fights between university students and townspeople. "Town and gown" fights, they were called. They began, in most instances, for no apparent reason except hatred, passed on for over two centuries, on the part of inhabitants of university towns for the university students. Many times, of course, there was provocation. The students were often boys and men of low moral character who cheated the townspeople. On the other hand, the townspeople often took advantage of the inexperience of young boys by charging exorbitant amounts for rooms, food, and drink.

Now Theo found himself unwittingly caught up in this bitter struggle. He was not afraid of a fight. His friends in the mines had long ago taught him the art of self-defense, both with fist and knife. But it seemed senseless to be fighting against people he did not know and with whom he had no personal quarrel. Still, if he had to — his grip on the knife tightened.

Now there was a clamor in the streets, voices shouting and running boots crashing on the cobblestones. Suddenly, through the open door appeared the figure of a helmeted man, wearing a steel breastplate and flourishing a long sword.

"Stand fast!" he shouted.

"The Guard!" cried one of the city men. The two groups, men and students, became a mass of milling individuals. Knives and pikestaffs disappeared as if by magic. Each person had but one thought: to get out of the tavern at once.

More guardsmen burst into the room. "Stand where you are!" they cried. These words only served to increase the commotion.

Theo felt a hand pulling at his elbow. It was Hans. "Follow me!" he said. Pushing and twisting in the turmoil, they made their way to a little door next to the fireplace. A moment later, the two had slipped out and were heading back to Frau Mueller's.

"Whew!" Theo wiped his brow. "That was lucky!"

"I spotted the waitresses and the spit boy sneaking out of that door."

"I wonder what will happen back there."

"Oh," said Hans, "those poor devils of townsmen will spend the night in jail, while the students go scot-free. The university is a separate corporation, you know, with special rights granted by the Pope and the Emperor. And the town really depends on the university for its living. So, unless a student commits a major crime, like murder, he can get away without punishment for almost any bad act. And students have been known to get away with murder, too!"

In their room, as they prepared for sleep, Theo said, "Hans!"

"Yes?"

"Do you realize that we never paid for our half-eaten dinner — and I'm still hungry!"

Hans's response was laughter and a pillow thrown at Theo's head.

Classes began the next day. Hans had to attend classes in the first area of learning, known as the trivium. This covered three subjects: grammar, rhetoric, and logic. Grammar concerned itself with a study of the classic writers of ancient Rome; the work was more advanced than in the monastery preparatory schools. In rhetoric, famous orations such as those of Cicero were studied. Also, some study was made of Roman law. In logic, the students learned the famous method of proof called the syllogism, developed by the great Aristotle. This subject was very important, for no one could graduate without being able to argue for or against the truth of any statement. One of the most famous examples of this kind of argument was the one which declared:

> *All men are mortal.*
> *Socrates is a man.*
> *Therefore, Socrates is mortal.*

Theo discovered, however, that medical students at Tübingen did not have to bother with the trivium; they began classes in medicine, botany, and anatomy at once. He was astounded, and later dismayed, to find that most of the professors simply read their lectures to the students. Moreover, most of their statements were copied from the books of ancient Greek and Roman doctors and scientists.

Besides the Greek "father of medicine," Hippocrates, there were three such ancient authorities whose words were accepted as truth by the university physicians. Their names were Celsus, Galen, and Avicenna. Celsus was a Roman writer who lived during the "Golden Age" of Roman culture and put together in a book all the medical knowledge of his time. He himself had not been a doctor, but he had written about medicine so beautifully and wisely that his book was still considered by the professors to contain a wealth of medical truths.

Galen was the most revered of the three. About 150 A.D., he had come as a young doctor to the city of Alexandria in Egypt. This city, under the reign of the Ptolemies, had become the cultural center of the world. Noted artists, poets, writers, scientists, and doctors came to Alexandria to teach, to learn, and to create. It did not take long for Galen to be recognized as one of the greatest physicians in the world. He wrote books on physiology, anatomy, diagnosis, and treatment which became as authoritative for physicians as the Bible was for theologians.

Avicenna was an Arab who was born almost nine hundred years after Galen, during the period when the Mohammedan people spread westward and conquered many of the countries that bordered on the Mediterranean Sea. The leaders of Islam, as their nation was called, encouraged the spread of knowledge; in their major cities, great artists and scientists taught and worked. The name Avicenna was actually a Latin version of the great doctor's Arabic name, Abu Ali al Hussein ibn Sina.

Avicenna's ideas about the practice of medicine were based more upon what he had read of Hippocrates, Aristotle, and Galen than upon actual experience. Yet he was such a brilliant student that his books were accepted as truth by the university doctors of western Europe. Like Galen's books, the works of Avicenna were regarded as sacred and completely true.

Yet it was difficult for Theo to believe that these men had known all there was to know about medicine. He remembered his father, Doctor Wilhelm, saying, "In spite of what is written in the books, much of nature is still a mystery to us." Everywhere in Germany, right in the city of Tübingen itself, people were dying of diseases, were being crippled and paralyzed, while physicians stood by helplessly. What good did it do to read about Galen's theory of the humors of the body in a book, when the misery of human pain and suffering was everywhere? In the streets, in the taverns, Theo watched people's faces. It seemed to him that he could separate the well from the sick; he could tell the yellow pallor caused by a jaundiced liver and the false healthy redness of the cheeks that came with the coughing sickness. The lectures at the university were dull and tasteless; the medical facts that could be read in the faces and the bodies of people were alive and exciting.

Nevertheless, Theo studied his lessons and passed his tests. The months of his freshman year sped like the blinks of an eyelid. Soon it would be time for a brief vacation, with a chance to see Doctor Wilhelm and Johann again at Villach.

One afternoon, as Theo and Hans sat studying in their room, there was a thumping on the door. "Come in, it's open," called Hans. One of Theo's fellow medical students rushed in, almost babbling with excitement.

"Quickly! Quickly! A dissection today! A dissection!"

"What in the devil is he screaming about?" asked Hans, as the student turned and fled down the stairs.

Theo had already put down his book and was putting on his robe. "This is a great occasion, Hans. They're going to dissect a body in the great lecture hall of the medical school. The professors are only allowed one body a year for this, sometimes two. Only seniors are supposed to go, but everybody comes. I've never seen one. Want to go?"

"A dissection? What do I want with a dissection? Still ——" Hans shrugged. "It can't be as dull as this book on logic I have to memorize. Lead on, medico!"

The lecture hall was already filled when Theo and Hans arrived, but they managed to find standing room near one of the doors. The hall was a great semicircular amphitheater, with the benches sloping gradually down toward the lecture platform, which was visible from every point in the room. On the platform was a long table with a sheet draped over it. Three people were on the platform. On a chair mounted high on a dais to the left of the table was the professor of anatomy. He sat with great dignity in his beautiful velvet robe crowned with a crimson hood. Before him on a stand was an open book, massive, with thick covers of smooth parchment. Near the table stood another robed man with a long stick in his hand.

53

Behind the table, and holding an edge of the sheet, was the third man. He wore a leather apron about his waist. At his feet was an iron bucket.

The professor made a sign and the doors were closed by attendants. The man with the apron flipped the sheet off the table, disclosing the corpse of a man.

"A thief, taken from the gallows this very morning," whispered one of the students near Theo.

"We will begin with the anatomy of the abdominal cavity," said the professor loudly. The man with the stick used it to point to the man's stomach.

"Who's that fellow with the pointer?" asked Hans in a whisper.

"The demonstrator. He points out the parts described by

the lecturer, who is reading from Avicenna. The barber-surgeon there is called the prosector. You'll see what he does in a moment."

Five or six instruments lay on the table beside the body. The prosector chose one, a razor-sharp knife, and, with an elaborate sweep of his hand, made a longitudinal cut through the skin and muscles of the stomach. The professor began to read, in a monotonous and rather nasal tone, a description of the stomach and intestines from the volume before him. As he mentioned a particular organ, the prosector lifted it from the body cavity with a pair of tongs and the demonstrator pointed to it. A moment later, the organ was flung into the bucket. From a corner of the hall, a small dog, cheered on by the students, came slinking across the floor to snatch a dainty morsel from the pail.

The professor paid no attention to these interruptions, but droned on and on from the anatomical descriptions of Avicenna. Theo found himself becoming angry as the lecture continued, with the prosector holding up the anatomical part for a brief moment as the other waved his pointer. What a stupid way to teach anatomy, he thought. How can a doctor learn anything about the human body this way? The entire proceedings filled him with disgust.

"Let's go, Hans." Turning, Theo saw that Hans's face was pasty white. Quickly, he steered his friend through the lecture hall door and out into the school courtyard. Hans's breath was coming in great gulps, and beads of sweat stood out on his forehead.

"Sit down, relax. Take a slow deep breath." Theo smiled. "Too much for you, Hans?"

Hans shook his head. "I didn't think I was such a sissy. I've seen men hurt before, and plenty of blood. But this — didn't it make you sick?"

"Sick!" roared Theo, to Hans's astonishment. "Sick? No, it didn't make me sick like you. But it made me sick to my stomach to think that doctors who will hold people's lives in their hands are being trained in such a stupid manner." Theo pointed to the lecture hall. "Look at those ignoramuses. Learning anatomy at a distance! Learning anatomy from a man who reads it out of a book! Ye gods and little fishes! Hans, those students are going out to practice medicine in a few years. They will make diagnoses about disease based on what's going on in there!"

"But," protested Hans, "isn't that the way medicine is taught everywhere?"

"If it is, God help mankind! Well, this finishes me with Tübingen. I want to be a doctor, not a walking package of quotations from Avicenna and Galen."

Hans had gotten to his feet, and was shakily following Theo, who had begun to stride away, shaking his fists and muttering. "Hey, wait for me! I'm your roommate, remember?" Then, as he caught up with Theo, Hans asked, "What will you do? Where will you go?"

"I don't know, Hans. Somewhere, there must be a university where I can learn medicine properly. As soon as this year is over, I'm going to find such a place."

"What about money? How will you live?"

"I'll manage. As for traveling, my legs are sturdy enough."

Hans shrugged his shoulders. "I know you well enough not to try and change that stubborn mind of yours. If you must go, go with God. But please, can't we first find a tavern where I can straighten out my stomach with a little good red wine? Isn't that the best prescription for queasiness, Doctor?"

"Bah! I see the trivium has only served to muddle your senses more!" Theo slapped his friend good-naturedly on the back. "Very well, let's head for the Red Donkey."

But as he strode ahead, he could hear Johann's sharp voice saying: "God has made the universe in a wonderful and mysterious way . . . the alchemist must search out all the clues . . . then, by practicing the art of alchemy in his laboratory, he will discover those secrets of nature that God meant man to discover . . ."

By practicing in his laboratory, said Theo to himself. Isn't that the way, perhaps, for the physician to discover the secrets of healing? Shouldn't there be a laboratory for medicine?

Chapter Three

THEO SAT IN HIS ROOM, near the window, reading the letter from Doctor Wilhelm again for the third time.

To My Dear Son, Theophrastus:

I do not question your decision to leave the University of Tübingen. You are old enough to know your own mind and heart. Your happiness is my one desire. It pains me to tell you that I can send but little money; you are welcome to what I have. Where will you go? I know nothing about the other medical schools in Germany. However, here is one bit of information. Do you remember my friend, Joachim von Waadt, the teacher, who used to visit our house in Villach? He is now the Rector of the University of Vienna. Perhaps he will help you achieve your goal. Write often and tell me of your prog-

*ress. May God be with you in your search for knowl-
edge.*

Your father,

WILHELM

P.S. Johann sends his best wishes.

He folded the letter carefully and stowed it in a pocket of his jerkin. Where would he go? And with so little money? The purse that had once bulged with gold and silver coins was now quite flat, and tied easily. Theo rose and walked to the door of his room. Which universities were better, he pondered, those to the north or to the northwest?

He closed Frau Mueller's front door behind him, still speculating on the merits of the various schools. To the north lay the universities of Heidelberg, Mainz, and Cologne. To the northwest were the universities of Wittenberg, Leipzig, and Erfurt. Which of these had the best medical school? He would have to ask someone at Tübingen. But who would know?

Looking up, he realized that he had strolled as far as the courtyard of the university. It was a mild spring day, one of the last vacation days before the end of the term. Students in twos and threes crossed the flat brick paving, chatting idly, their black gowns trailing and flapping in the warm breeze.

Theo observed some unusual activity under an archway in one corner of the court. There, a group of seven students were busy making up bundles of food, rolling blankets into packs, and tying books into packages with string. Curious, he sauntered nearer.

"Are you fellows going on a trip?" he inquired of the student nearest to him.

"Does it look as though we're baking bread?" The sullen-faced student bent to his task of rolling a blanket pack.

"Ah, don't be such a churl, Otto," called out one of the others. "We're going north," he said to Theo. "Up to Heidelberg with the other wandering scholars."

"Wandering scholars?"

"You must be a new boy! Haven't you ever heard of the wandering scholars? We taste the learning to be had at all universities, because there's no one place that can give us enough. And since we can't afford to ride in fancy carriages, we walk."

"But how do you live? What do you eat?"

Another student looked up. "Easy enough, little brother," he answered. "We live off the land. There are many things an educated person can do for the poor, ignorant farmers. Medical students can pull bad teeth and prescribe medicines. Theology students can help at christenings, perform last rites for the dying, or confess the wicked. Law students can help settle those little disputes which are always springing up among neighbors. And the farmers repay us with fat geese and hens, with grain, and with shelter." He winked. "And some of the country girls are pretty, too!"

An idea began to form in Theo's head. "Look, when are you leaving?"

"Tomorrow at cockcrow."

Theo spoke with growing excitement. "My name is Theophrastus von Hohenheim. I'm a medical student. May I join you?"

"We have enough already," growled the surly student, to whom Theo had first spoken.

"Ah, Otto, that is nonsense." The student who seemed to be the spokesman for the group stood up and came over to Theo. "This chap seems able to take care of himself. You know that an extra hand is always good to have, especially if it comes to a tussle. How about it," he addressed Theo, "are you afraid of a scrap?"

Theo grinned and patted the scabbard of his knife. "I eat at the Red Donkey," he said.

The other scholars laughed. The one next to Theo held out his hand. "You're our man!" he cried, shaking Theo's hand warmly. "And besides," he added, "we have no medicos this trip. People always respect a doctor."

"I'll go and pack now," said Theo. His heart was beating with wild elation.

"First meet everybody. My name is Richard Clapham — I'm English. Going around the circle: Jacques Duprés, France; Olaf Swenson, Sweden; Adolf von Meister, Prussia; Rob MacLarin, Scotland; Pierre Fleury, France; Otto Palacz, Bohemia."

Each of the students nodded in turn, except for the last, who bent, muttering, over the thongs of his pack. Theo walked over and, stooping a little, scanned Otto's face with concern.

"Have you just had your dinner?" he asked.

"What the devil does that have to do with you?" snarled Otto, who was rather short and stout and tended to wheeze a little when he bent over.

Theo kept talking, as though he had not heard Otto at all. "From the color of your face and the sound of your breathing, I'd guess that you have a bit of a stomach-ache going on now.

And I'd guess that your pulse would be rather fast and some-what irregular, which means that you're building up to a good case of indigestion. No wonder you're snarling at everyone; I would too, if my belly hurt as much as yours. Did you have the boiled cabbage at the Red Donkey this noon?"

Rather dazed by Theo's words, Otto nodded his head dumbly.

"Yes, the cabbage, that's it! Overspiced it was, and the consistence of tree bark. I remember telling Hans it would probably give two out of three customers a stomach-ache."

"But — but —" stammered Otto, "h-how the devil did you know?"

"Observation, Otto. Observation and common sense, two things the university medical professors never seem to mention in their lectures. Well, come along to my room. I'll brew you up some wine with mint and fennel seed. That's a prescription of my father's that always seems to work."

The heads of the other students were nodding and their hands waved as they excitedly discussed Theo's ability to diagnose Otto's indigestion. "Hey," cried one, "he's the sort we want along, all right! If he can do that kind of guessing for the farmers, we'll be dining well this trip. What do you say, Otto?"

Still somewhat dazed, Otto admitted that Theo seemed to be a useful chap. Then, with a look of awe on his face, he rose to his feet and lumbered after the beckoning finger of Theo like a tame bear following its master.

Just before he reached the university gate, Theo turned and waved. "See you at cockcrow, gentlemen! Come along, friend Otto."

That night, Hans and Theo sat talking long after their usual bedtime. A single candle, already dripped down to a short white stub, filled the room with shadows.

"But with the wandering ones!" Hans exclaimed for the tenth time, striking the desk with a fist. "Have you any idea of their reputation?"

"If they are at all like the chaps I met today," said Theo, "then all the things you've heard are a lot of old wives' tales! They seem like very decent fellows."

"Will your father approve of your becoming an itinerant beggar?"

"Now listen, Hans! Item one: my money supply is low. How else am I to find a good medical school? Item two: my father trusts my good judgment. He ought to; he taught me how to exercise it. No, my mind is made up. I'm off in the morning for Heidelberg." Theo stood up and reached over to place his hand on Hans's shoulder. "But I shall miss you, old friend!"

"And I you, Theo." Hans rose, also, and they stood for a moment, hands on each other's shoulders. Then Hans lifted his hand and thumped Theo on the back. "Off to bed with you, or else you'll never see cockcrow!"

"You're right, it's late," cried Theo. He began to shuck the clothes from his body feverishly, and fell into bed just as Hans blew out the guttering candle flame.

At dawn, when the eastern sky had begun to redden, the North Gate of Tübingen was opened. Theo and his companions were part of the jostling crowd of wayfarers swarming out on the main road to Heidelberg. There were beggars in torn hose and ragged cloaks, shuffling along in mismatched shoes, using long wooden staffs to aid them on their way. Here

and there in the group were peddlers, bearing great packs on their backs. These men went from farmhouse to farmhouse, selling such items as cheap jewelry, religious pictures, or pieces of silk cloth to the housewives. As was the custom, every man was armed, with a knife or a dagger fixed in his belt.

Theo walked along with the English student, Richard Clapham. "Tell me, Richard," he asked, "how do you pay tuition at the different universities?"

Richard laughed. "Tuition? Most of us have no money for such a luxury. We just go to the most popular lectures. They're so crowded with students that no one knows the difference."

"How do you get credit toward a bachelor's degree?"

"That's a different story. There are usually scholarships for

poor students. Or, better still, one tries to find a wealthy patron. There are ways and ways. Personally, I'm a taster. I like to sip at the best cups of learning and keep moving."

A mile down the road, they were joined by another band of scholars coming up from the east. There was an exchange of greetings, and they moved on toward Heidelberg together. After a brief period of gossip, a telling and retelling of the latest news about professors and lectures at the various universities of Europe, one of the scholars struck up a song. All the others joined in. The tune was a merry one and the words were Latin:

> *"Stilus nam et tabule*
> *Sunt feriales epule,*
> *et Nasonis carmina*
> *vel aliorum pagina . . ."*

Richard nudged Theo. "Come on, sing with us, Theo!"

"But I've never heard this song."

"It's called 'Vacation Time.' The wandering scholars have been singing it for over two hundred years."

Theo listened carefully; the second time around, he sang loudly and happily with the others:

"Freedom flutters in the air!
Textbooks hidden, slates are bare,
Dust and cobwebs overfall
Latin classics, one and all!
Let the cursed schoolbooks rot —
Now we celebrate our lot,
Dancing, singing, all at play —
Hiho, Scholars, let's away!"

When the sun was at its highest point, they all stopped for lunch. In a grove of green shade trees just off the road, the students shared pieces of cold meat and bread. A brook that welled up from between some rocks gave them cold water to drink. After a short rest, they headed north again.

Theo noticed that the tradespeople tended to group themselves near the scholars. He mentioned this to Richard.

"That's because of the highwaymen."

"Highwaymen!"

"Yes. Some of those peddlers keep a sizable amount of money on their persons. Alone, a peddler is easy prey for a robber. But we scholars are a rather large company. Since we have a reputation for being poor, few robbers bother to attack us. So these tradesmen like to stay near us for protection."

A newcomer had slowly moved up from the rear until he

reached Theo's group. He was an older man, with a white beard and long white hair. He wore fancy breeches tied at the knee, a velvet coat, and a wide-brimmed velvet hat. He led behind him, at the end of a long rope, a bony, sway-backed nag, loaded from haunches to neck with bulging packs. Hanging from one of the packs was a small banner inscribed with insignia which Theo recognized at once. The emblems were those of Saint Cosmas and Saint Damian, patron saints of the guild of barber-surgeons.

The barber-surgeons were men who practiced those particular medical arts which the academic physicians disdained. Few university doctors would soil their hands by performing surgical operations, bleeding patients, or dissecting bodies. This "manual labor" was left for the surgeon. Most poor people could not afford the fees charged by physicians; such patients had to depend upon the services of the barber-surgeons. Sometimes the surgeon was skilled in his trade, sometimes he was an ignorant quack. There was no way for the patient to distinguish between skill and ignorance.

Theo moved over until he was abreast of the surgeon and hailed him. "Where are you bound for, Master Surgeon?"

The old man smiled, happy to have company. He spoke in a peasant dialect. "Everywhere and anywhere, my boy. Jacob Bader is the name, better known as Old Jacob the Barber. Perhaps you'd be liking a little blood let from your veins to relieve the summer heat? With Old Jacob's skilled hand it's guaranteed to be a painless job."

Theo smiled. "I'm Theophrastus von Hohenheim, from Tübingen medical school."

Jacob's manner changed. His face became an expressionless mask. "Oh? Beg your pardon, sir, I didn't know you were one of them."

"Come now, Master Bader," chided Theo, "don't be afraid of me. I am not one of your snobbish university physicians. My father always said that a knowledge of the art of surgery was most important in medicine."

"And who might your father be, young fellow?"

"Wilhelm von Hohenheim, of Villach."

"Doctor Wilhelm! Why, of course! A great man, your father. Not like the others of his profession. I met him some years ago in Switzerland. Let's see, where was it? Ein — Ein —"

"Einsiedeln."

"That's the place. Pleasant little village, as I remember."

Just saying the name brought a rush of memories into Theo's mind. He saw the mountains above the walls of the abbey, the foaming river Sihl rushing through the village, the Devil's Bridge, and his grandmother standing in the road, waving farewell. How long ago all that seemed!

He turned to the surgeon. "Will you walk with me, Master Bader, and tell me something about the art of surgery?"

"Aye, young man, that I will. It's rare to find a medical man willing to learn from the likes of me. Oh, those university doctors, they walk around like butter wouldn't melt in their mouths. But you ask the folks around the countryside who does the healing. 'Old Jacob the Barber,' they'll tell you. You know what those fancy doctors say? 'God is the healer, the physician is his assistant.' Nonsense, say I. *I'm* the healer. I let the blood from their veins. I purge them of the bad humours. I cut the poison out of their bodies."

His eyes took on a sly look. "Of course, for them that choose to believe that only God does it, I have items that heal too. Sure, I sell holy charms and good luck pieces and blessed salves! But the real healing — that's Old Jacob the Barber's work!"

Theo was fascinated. During the entire journey, he plied the barber-surgeon with question after question. And Jacob, happy to find someone interested in his work, gave Theo an insight into all his techniques.

There was a sudden halloo from the students in the front of the march. Looking in the direction of their outstretched hands, Theo saw the turrets of the Heidelberg castle high above the Neckar River. The stone walls loomed fierce and impregnable over the eastern part of the town.

At the gates of Heidelberg, Theo and Jacob Bader said their farewells. "Chance might be that I'll pass through Villach one of these days," said the old man, shaking Theo's hand. "I'll tell Doctor Wilhelm I saw you."

"Thank you, sir," said Theo. "And I'm grateful for everything I've learned." As Jacob led his plodding horse away, Theo cried after him, "God be with you on your journeys!"

There was a tug at Theo's elbow. "Come along, Theo," cried Richard Clapham. "It's getting late. Adolf von Meister has been to Heidelberg before; he knows which doors are open to us."

An hour later, the eight comrades found themselves in the magnificent home of a nobleman, a friend of von Meister's father. Their host bade them welcome. There was water for a bath and a hot supper on the table. Well, Theo said to himself, the life of a wanderer isn't so bad, after all!

69

But the University of Heidelberg proved to be a great disappointment. Theo found there the same stagnant methods of
teaching as at Tübingen. The professors merely read their lectures from books. The medicine was the medicine of Galen
and Avicenna.

"It makes me furious!" cried Theo. He and his friends were
sitting before the fireplace in the parlor of the nobleman's
house. "This is a time of change, of discovery. Hasn't the news
reached Germany that a new world has been discovered on the
other side of the ocean? Why, I heard about that in Villach
when I was just a boy. A man named Columbus sailed out of
Spain the year before I was born and discovered the eastern
shores of the Orient! Yet these miserable medical professors

are content to recite over and over again, like schoolboys, writings that are over a thousand years old."

"But — but —" puffed the stout Otto, "to fly in the face of the venerated authorities! Why — why — it just isn't done!"

"And besides," put in the Frenchman, Fleury, "where is it any different? I can assure you that at the University of Paris things are even worse."

Theo thrust out a stubborn jaw. "I'll find a place where medicine is taught properly if I have to travel the length and breadth of the world! And if no such place exists, why then, I'll just have to find out for myself."

"Bravo, Doctor Theo!" cried Swenson. "When you have finished, don't forget to come to Sweden and reform our universities."

"I know you're laughing at me," said Theo, "but I mean it. I'm leaving Heidelberg tomorrow." He fell silent, a scowl over his face.

"Tomorrow?" cried Richard Clapham. "You aren't serious!" He looked at Theo's face. "Well, I guess you are. Don't glower, my friend. We're all on your side. But you'll have to learn to keep your sense of humor."

"This matter isn't funny to me!" But looking from one grinning face to another, Theo could no longer sulk. He leaped to his feet and faced his friends. "Well, how about a farewell party?"

"That's the best idea you've had today, von Hohenheim," cried Adolf. "I'll find our host and get him to donate a few bottles of good wine."

Theo sighed. "Ah, me, I shall miss the sight of your ugly faces. Ohhh!" He staggered and toppled backward to the floor as a hand reached out and pulled his ankle. The conversation gave way to a good-natured wrestling match.

First Heidelberg, and then Mainz. From Mainz, Theo walked to Cologne, due north. There he found a city that had fallen upon hard times. Business was bad; there was unemployment. Beggars crowded the streets. "It's the fault of the Jews," said one merchant to Theo. But another told him, "The trouble is that the Jews were expelled from Cologne about ninety years ago, and business has never been the same since. Why don't these administrators learn that such bigotry gets people nowhere?"

The most beautiful sight in Cologne was the cathedral. Theo never tired of looking at the magnificent arches and the sculptured stone figures. He went to Mass there every morning just to feel the beauty about him.

The university, however, was another matter. There, Theo found no beauty, only the stilted parroting that was typical of the other places of higher learning. Cologne became unbearably dull for him; he felt he must leave. But where could he go now?

As he sat in a quiet corner of the Cologne market place, packing his knapsack, a piece of paper fluttered to the ground. Stooping to pick it up, he saw that it was the letter he had received in Tübingen from Doctor Wilhelm. One of the sentences caught his eye: ". . . is now the Rector of the University of Vienna. Perhaps he will help you . . ."

Vienna? Why not! He had heard that the University of Vienna was the best school in all the German lands. And Joachim von Waadt a rector — that was a true stroke of luck!

Theo finished rolling his blanket and slung it with the pack over his shoulder. He stopped in the market place only long enough to buy a loaf of hard, black peasant bread. Soon he had passed through the gate of the south wall of Cologne. He had already mapped his route: follow the Rhine River south to the town of Freiburg, then east along the Danube River to Ingolstadt, and finally to Vienna.

It was a long journey that took many weeks. But he was seeing parts of the Holy Roman Empire that he had never seen before. Freiburg lay in the middle of the Black Forest, a region so beautiful Theo hated to leave. There was a University of Freiburg, also; however, Theo found it to be a place where the students cared more for drinking and roughhousing than for learning. On he went to Ingolstadt, for a taste of the university life in that town. The professors there, he discovered, had not given birth to a new idea since the founding of the university in 1472.

Theo had formed the habit of carrying writing materials in his pack so that he could jot down his impressions of the universities he visited. For Freiburg, he wrote: ". . . more like a playhouse than a university"; and for Ingolstadt, he noted: ". . . a place full of stuffy old scholars."

On the road, he learned many lessons: how to be alone with himself for days, how to appear trusting and yet not trust strangers, how to talk a suspicious farmer into giving him a meal and a place to sleep, how to wheedle a pretty goosegirl into inviting him home for supper. He had a way with the common folk — the beggars and the charlatans on the road, the peasants who lived by the wayside. Their initial mistrust of the young scholar disappeared as he talked. Theo had spent

his boyhood among the peasants of Einsiedeln and the miners of Villach; he knew their simple ways and could speak their language.

Occasionally, on the highway, Theo could hear from afar the tinkling of a bell. This sound would herald the approach of a lone traveler dressed in a black cloak and a tall black hat. Great white patches were sewn on these garments. When such a person came near, the other travelers would crowd over on the side of the road as far away from him as they could get. Many made the sign of the cross and cried out, "Unclean! Unclean!"

This wanderer, who was required by law to wear a bell that would warn others of his approach, was a victim of the disease known as leprosy. No one knew the cause of leprosy, nor how it spread. But everyone knew its results: the rotting of the flesh, the foul sores that overspread the body, the fingers that became only little nubs of skin and bone. Doctor Wilhelm had told Theo how lepers were required to go to special hospitals called leprosaria. They were forbidden to frequent places where people were apt to gather, such as market places, churches, or inns. Even doctors were afraid to treat the disease. Theo remembered how his father spoke with scorn of the physicians who wore masks over their faces and long heavy gloves, and who used a stick to keep the lepers at a respectful distance.

"A doctor should not fear disease," Doctor Wilhelm had declared; "he ought to go out and challenge it."

Remembering his father's words, Theo did not run from the lepers. He looked closely at their faces and noted the various symptoms of the disease. He spoke to the lepers without fear, asking if they felt pain in different parts of the body. When he had money to spare, he would drop a copper coin or two into a piteously outstretched hand. While the other travelers marveled at his daring, Theo would calmly pause to add to his carefully kept notes on leprosy.

Vienna was the best fortified city Theo had ever seen. There was a double set of protecting walls marking off inner and outer parts of the city. The Emperor Maximilian feared that the Turkish infidels would swarm up the valley of the Danube to attack Vienna, just as they had come up the Drave River to attack Villach.

The University of Vienna was larger than any of the other universities Theo had visited. The buildings were handsome and the decorations lavish. Waiting in the anteroom of the rector's apartment, Theo felt threadbare and ragged. But the mention of Theo's name brought the head of the university hurrying out of his study.

"Theophrastus von Hohenheim! How good to see you again!" Joachim von Waadt was a ruddy-faced man with white hair. He encircled Theo in the folds of his soft velvet robe with a fond embrace. "Though I must say you've grown since we last met."

Theo was pleased. How wonderful to be on such good terms with a high university official! "Father wrote and suggested I come to see you, sir."

"I know, I know. He wrote to me also and said you might be coming this way. Here, let me see —" The rector held Theo away at arm's length. "Hmmm, you do look a bit thin. How do you like the life of the wandering scholar?" He stopped and looked about. "Dear me, what an ill-mannered old man I am becoming. Come inside, come inside. You must be tired — and hungry, too, I'll wager. I'll have some food brought in at once."

"Thank you, Doctor von Waadt."

"Oh, I ought to tell you. I am better known here by my Latin name — Vadianus. You know, it's the custom at universities for those who have attained the doctor's degree to assume a Latin name. But I'm keeping you on your feet. Put down your pack — sit here. Now, tell me about your adventures."

Theo was hungry. Between luscious bites of roast chicken, he told Vadianus of his wanderings and his disappointments.

"Ever since I received your father's letter," said the rector, "I have been thinking about you. Here, have some more of that chicken. More wine? But I waited to see what kind of student you were. Hmmm . . . yes, you will need some new clothes. Frankly, Theo, I like what I see. Now, how would you like to qualify for the medical school here at the university? I think we have a good faculty here, at least better than any other university in Germany. For example, we don't admit a student to the medical school until he has obtained his bachelor's degree. Now you must admit that gives us students of better caliber."

Theo swallowed a mouthful of wine. "That's true."

"I would consider you experienced enough to be ready for the bachelor of arts degree in about two years. That means you only study the quadrivium: philosophy, astronomy, music, and arithmetic. I shall be happy to sponsor you, and you may lodge here in my apartment. Well, young Master von Hohenheim, what do you say to that?"

Theo's mouth was wide open; he was speechless.

Theo was disappointed at the thought of having to begin by studying subjects other than medicine. But gradually his interest in the quadrivium, especially in astronomy and natural philosophy, deepened. He remembered how the alchemist Johann had told him that a knowledge of the motions of the planets and the stars was essential to a proper understanding of alchemical reactions. Natural philosophy dealt with all the happenings in nature: the causes of the motion of bodies, the causes of heat and coldness in things, and many other phenomena. These had been explained in the writings of Aristotle, the ancient Greek philosopher and scientist. Nineteen hundred years before, he had tried to explain in a logical way all that happened in the universe.

Two years passed so quickly that graduation day seemed to come as a surprise to Theo. He had passed his thesis examination, thanks to the training he had received at Lavanttal and the fatherly assistance of Vadianus. The Rector of the University forced Theo to speak always in Latin. Patiently, he corrected Theo's mistakes. When the time came for the dispute in which all graduating students had to engage, Theo acquitted himself well.

"Well, Theo, now you are a bachelor of arts!" It was Vadianus who spoke. He and Theo were walking back from the graduation ceremony. Theo was very proud of the colored bachelor's hood draped over his shoulders. "I suppose you're looking forward to medical school."

"Why, sir, I —" Theo seemed at a loss for words.

"No need to say anything more — it's all arranged. I've entered your name as a medical student for the semester following this vacation. Don't worry about the tuition and fees."

"But, sir, I —"

"And I want no thanks. It's the least I can do for the son of my friend, Wilhelm. You've worked hard, Theo, and you have earned your opportunity."

What Theo had been trying to say was that he had attended some of the lectures at the medical school. It was the same story as before. Even at the great University of Vienna, the medical professors taught medicine out of books, not from experience. In his disappointment, Theo had already decided to leave Vienna.

However, he could not bring himself to tell this to Vadianus. The old man walked by Theo's side as proudly as though he were Theo's own father. I might as well stay at Vienna, Theo decided. One medical school or another — the important thing was to become a doctor.

Nature intervened to help him. In the first hot weeks of that summer, the rats of Vienna came out of their holes to die in the streets. First the rats, then the people. The plague had come to Vienna. Noblemen and wealthy citizens fled from the city. People who remained began to die faster than the rats.

All day long, the church bells clanged a requiem for the dead. Carts filled with bodies rattled through the streets to the great burying trenches dug outside the city walls. There, as a black-robed monk solemnly chanted the burial rites, the corpses were flung into mass graves. Men, so desperately poor they would work at anything for a few coins, quickly shoveled earth into a filled grave and then moved on to the next.

Even the physicians of Vienna were afraid of the plague and hastened from the stricken city. The few who stayed to treat patients demanded outrageous fees. A doctor entering the house of a plague patient took care to cover himself from head to foot with a special robe of heavy material. Over his face he wore a mask with a beaklike nose. Inside the nose was a sponge soaked with vinegar and aromatic herbs, as protection from the plague.

The university was officially closed. Theo took advantage of the confusion to bid Vadianus farewell. There were tears in the old man's eyes.

"The plague will not last forever, Theo. Return to Vienna soon."

"I will, sir. And thank you for all you have done." One last embrace, and Theo was on his way through the streets of the stricken city. The smell of death hung over Vienna. As he walked rapidly toward the northern gate, Theo saw many doors nailed shut with great wooden crossbars. These houses had become sealed tombs for dying victims of the plague. From behind some of the doors came the hopeless groans of those who had been shut up alive in their own homes.

Once past the gate, Theo took the northern road that led to the other great universities of Germany: Wittenberg, Leipzig, and Erfurt. At a rise in the road, he stopped and looked back. A pall of smoke hung over the city of Vienna — smoke from the fumigation fires, from the burning piles of victims' clothing, and from some burning houses in the poor quarter of the city.

There must be a way to fight the plague, he said to himself. When I become a doctor, I will find that way. And I will not be afraid!

Northward, the road wound through the beautiful forests of Bohemia, into green meadowlands, past towns where there was no more talk of plague. The journey from Vienna to Wittenberg took many weeks. Again Theo found that he had taken a fruitless journey. From Wittenberg to Leipzig, from Leipzig to Erfurt, it was all the same. The same sentences from the books of Galen and Avicenna were recited by the medical professors at their lectures. Students attended the same dreary, once-a-year anatomy dissections. The result was the same group of newly graduated physicians, proud and splendid in their velvet robes, ready to apply their carefully memorized prescriptions to live, sick human beings.

"They are only sham doctors," Theo wrote in his notes. "No university in Germany turns out a single doctor with the practical knowledge of medicine that my father has. These charlatans are only interested in money, not in human lives. They don't care how many people they kill, as long as they do it in the holy names of Galen, Celsus, and Avicenna."

At Wittenberg, he found some brief excitement. A professor of theology named Martin Luther had been saying some daring things in his lectures. He had accused the men at the head of the Papal State in Rome of being negligent in their duties toward God and man. The university had divided into two factions, for Luther and against. Arguments were heard day and night; the air was tense. Theo stayed awhile and listened, and became bored. Theology seemed to be all words; he wanted knowledge that came from getting at the roots of things. He wanted to know all that could be known about life and death and sickness, about pain and fever and running sores.

The year 1512 had come. Theo had tasted the offerings at the Universities of Leipzig and Erfurt and had found them wanting. In despair, he turned his face southward and began the long journey homeward.

"By heavens, I just can't believe my eyes!" It was the same room in the little house in Villach. Doctor Wilhelm stood clasping Theo by the shoulders. "You were only a boy when you left. You've come back a man!"

Theo grinned and threw his head back, inhaling the sweet familiar fragrances of medicine and birch-wood smoke. How many times in the last year he had sat shivering in the dark next to a little, smoking fire, dreaming about this room and everything in it!

Theo looked at his father. Doctor Wilhelm was five years older, too. The black hair had begun to gray. The face was creased with little lines. But the same kind expression, the same understanding smile was still there.

They dined together, and for Theo it was a feast. He told his father stories of the Red Donkey in Tübingen that made the doctor roar with laughter. Later, over a cup of hot mulled wine, Theo talked of his disappointments and his ambitions.

"Tell me, Father, what am I to do? Which way shall I go now?"

Doctor Wilhelm sipped at his cup. "Theo, you are a young man in a strange time. There are many changes going on. Men are voyaging to distant lands, places no one even dreamed of only twenty-five years ago. And you? Your search for knowledge is part of that change, Theo. I'm only a small-town physician and a practical alchemist. I'll never be a great man. But the chance is there for you."

"What do you mean, Father?"

"There is a place in Europe where men speak of new ways in medicine."

Theo started up. "Where? Where?"

"Italy. I hear that in the Italian universities men with new and bold vision are teaching medicine."

"Then Italy is where I must go!"

The doctor smiled. "I'm glad to see that behind that mature face is the same excitable boy I knew. Listen to me. The road to Italy has just been opened by our Swiss army. They and the Emperor Maximilian have conquered all Lombardy. So, down you go through the Brenner Pass to Milan with safe passage. And there you are, in the land of new ideas!"

Theo had leaped to his feet. He drained the wine from his cup and set it on the table with a crash. "And which university is the best, Father? Do you know?"

"Padua, perhaps. No, wait, I remember hearing some good things about the University of Ferrara. The rulers of Ferrara, the Duke d'Este and his wife, Lucrezia Borgia, are friendly to the Swiss. I have been told they have attracted some very learned men to the university. As for the medical school, there's a man teaching there, a Doctor Leoniceno, whose wisdom has reached as far as Villach."

"Ferrara it is, then." Theo crouched before the fire for a moment, and then jumped to his feet again. "Father, I can't wait. I must leave for Italy first thing in the morning!"

"But, Theo, you have just —" Doctor Wilhelm read the desperate want in his son's eyes. "Of course, you must go tomorrow. To bed at once, then, my boy. You'll want to be rested and fresh." Then, as Theo opened his mouth, "No, no!

I'm the doctor here. And that's my prescription. Ah me, Johann will be unhappy about not seeing you."

"And I about not seeing him, Father. But Ferrara —"

"Yes, I know. Come to think of it, I've put aside a bit of money for which I have no use. Perhaps it will come in handy for you. Now I'd better see if your room is ready."

As the doctor left, Theo turned and stared into the fire. The embers snapped and sparks flew. Thoughts danced in his head like the flames. He was like a man with a great thirst.

For Theo had decided to become the best doctor in the world.

Chapter Four

PROFESSOR NICCOLO LEONICENO was the oldest man Theo had ever seen. His velvet cap sat awry on the few white hairs still sprouting from his balding scalp. The leathery skin of his face was very crinkled. He walked slowly, using a long wooden staff to support his bent figure.

Yet, at the age of eighty-five, his mind possessed the brilliance of youth. He had the keenest eye in all Italy for spotting the symptoms of diseases. Noblemen and wealthy citizens begged him to attend at their sickbeds. He was the most popular lecturer at the medical school of the University of Ferrara — as some wits put it, Leoniceno *was* the medical school.

"You know," explained one of Theo's fellow students, "Ferrara really has the reputation of being a diploma mill. Anyone with enough gold pieces to spend can buy his college degree here."

"Except in the medical school," said another. "Old Leoniceno has seen to that. His students have to work like demons."

Theo was drawn to this teacher. The old physician, in turn, began to notice that Theo was different from the other students. After a lecture, it was usually Theo who came forward to ask the most disturbing questions. One afternoon, Professor Leoniceno signaled Theo to follow him. "Let us go to my study, young man. I want to have a chat with you."

Theo was delighted. "Yes, sir." He followed the professor eagerly.

In the study, Theo felt as though he had entered a gold mine. There were shelves laden with fascinating specimens of animal and human skeletons and medicinal plants. One side of the room was a wall of books, from the handwritten manuscripts of olden times to the latest volumes from metal-type presses. In one corner, Theo spied a few pieces of alchemical apparatus.

"Just a little hobby of mine." The old man had followed Theo's gaze. "A little dabbling in the arts. I know it's not fashionable for a doctor —"

"But that's where you're wrong!"

Theo blushed and put his hand over his mouth. How rudely he had spoken to this great man!

Professor Leoniceno did not seem to be shocked. He blinked his pale blue eyes, pointed to a chair, and said calmly, "Sit down, young man. Now, tell me what you meant by that."

Excitedly, Theo told him of his father, Doctor Wilhelm, who was both a good doctor and a fine alchemist. He talked about Johann and the mysteries of nature. The professor listened patiently without a word. When Theo had finished, he asked quietly, "Would you rather be an alchemist than a physician?"

"No!" cried Theo, jumping to his feet. "Both! Both! A doctor must be an alchemist! He must experiment with all kinds of compounds, not just plant drugs. There are too many old fools who look to astrology for cures, who follow only the prescriptions of Avicenna and Galen. They kill more patients than they cure. I think — oh, forgive me, Professor Leoniceno, I didn't mean — I —I —" Theo began to stutter with embarrassment.

"Don't apologize, young man. You are right, there *are* too many old fools in this profession. And proud fools, too, afraid to admit their ignorance. I've been fighting them all my life. Look here!"

He selected a book from his library and handed it to Theo, who translated the long Latin title aloud. *"Errors I Have Noticed in the Works of Pliny and Other Ancient Authors Who Wrote About Medicine.* Why, sir, you dared to attack the authority of the great Roman historian, Pliny?"

"I wrote that book over twenty years ago — before you were born, I'll wager. Oh, Pliny was a great historian. But his medical facts! A mixture of magic and old wives' tales, my boy. Oh yes, this volume came as a great shock to my friends. The learned men of Europe sprang to Pliny's defense. All fools, proud fools, unable to separate fancy from fact."

"May I borrow this, sir? This is the first courageous piece of work I've ever —"

"Courageous?" Leoniceno threw back his head and cackled with laughter. "Courage is cheap, my boy!" He leaned forward, and his eyes now burned with the same fire as Theo's. "Evidence! That's what is needed to defeat the ones who cringe before ancient authority, who are afraid to believe even their own eyes. *Evidence!*"

Theo was choked with emotion. He knew now that his search was ended. The fruitless years of wandering from school to school were over.

"Young man —" Leoniceno was all business again. "I asked you to come here for a reason. Confound it — my memory is failing again — what is your name?"

"Theophrastus von Hohenheim, sir."

"Hmmm, von Hohenheim, yes . . . Well, Master von Hohenheim, how would you like to become a sort of special assistant working with me? We'll call it a scholarship, if you like — waiver of tuition, and all that. I like you. I believe that you will become not only a good doctor but a doctor with vision. That's a rare quality nowadays. Well, will you accept?"

And on that day, in a little room in the medical school of Ferrara, Theo became one of the initiates. His appetite for learning was insatiable. All that Professor Leoniceno could teach him, he swallowed in a gulp, and begged for more. Theo's greatest joy was that Leoniceno seemed to be an endless source of new medical ideas.

Galen's medical theories had followed the pattern of Aristotelian thinking. Like the four elements, Fire, Air, Earth, and Water, with their qualities, Hot, Dry, Cold, and Wet, the human body contained four humors, Blood, Phlegm, Black Bile, and Yellow Bile. Medical students had to memorize a little diagram that would make this clear:

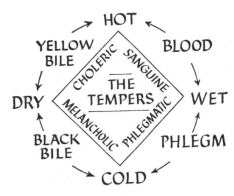

The balance or imbalance of the four tempers, Sanguine, Phlegmatic, Melancholic, and Choleric caused health or disease. A sanguine person, therefore, had too much blood and was sent to the surgeon to be bled; a choleric person would probably feel bilious.

Galen believed that remedies for illnesses had to be made of drugs whose qualities were opposite to those of the humors causing the particular disease. "Opposite cures opposite" was the law handed down to future doctors in the medical schools. If a doctor diagnosed a disease as phlegmatic — that is, related to the cold-wet qualities of the phlegmatic humor — he would call upon the pharmacist to fill a prescription containing drugs whose qualities were hot-dry.

"Don't speak so disparagingly about Celsus," said Professor Leoniceno to Theo one day.

"But he didn't even practice medicine. You said so yourself!"

"That's true. But he was a very clever and understanding man. Here, hand me that volume of Celsus — over there, on the desk." Leoniceno leafed rapidly through the pages.

"There, see how he lists remedies? According to their effects — their specific virtues. Look at this: emetics — to cause vomiting; diaphoretics — to cause sweating; narcotics — to cause sleep. Does that look like Galen's humor theory to you?"

Theo was amazed. "I never realized Celsus was so advanced!" All that day, he thought only of the arrangement of specific qualities of remedies.

The next morning, he could not wait. An hour before lecture time, he was thumping at Professor Leoniceno's door. The old doctor flung it open in surprise.

"Theo! What a clatter! Is something wrong?"

Theo rushed past him into the study, talking rapidly over his shoulder.

"What? What?" cried Leoniceno, closing the door. "Stop babbling, man! What is it?"

Theo stopped and took a deep gulp of air. "Celsus! His list of specific remedies — it's good! But it's not good enough. We have to know what is *in* the specific remedy that does the work. What is the substance in a certain plant that makes the plant an emetic? That's the important question to ask. And this question can be answered by alchemy!"

Leoniceno said nothing. He only stared at Theo.

Theo hung his head. "I know you think I'm a fool."

The professor came forward and put his hands on Theo's shoulders. "On the contrary, young man," he said, "if you keep this up, you may become the best doctor in the whole world!"

"Yes," said Theo simply. "I am going to be better than Galen — better even than Celsus."

"As the Greeks would put it," grinned Professor Leoniceno, "you are going to be *Para*-Celsus — *beyond* Celsus."

"Sir," cried Theo, "I am inspired by you. Since it is the custom for university people to call themselves by Latin or classical names, I will do so, too. From this day on, I shall be known as Paracelsus!"

For the next two years, Theo soaked up knowledge like a sponge. Professor Leoniceno was always there, guiding, directing, pointing out the strengths and weaknesses of medical ideas.

"They say that this new sickness that has struck the army — the French disease — is caused by certain ill-timed conjunctions of the stars. Superstitious nonsense! I believe that the disease comes from pollution of the drinking water caused by flooding rivers and streams."

"Don't memorize the anatomy of Galen, my boy. His anatomy is based on the dissection of animals, not men."

"My colleagues in other countries curse me for saying this, Paracelsus; but I advise you to learn surgery. In our Italian medical schools, we have learned that the separation of surgery from the rest of medicine is an abomination."

Soon it was time for graduation. The awarding of the doctor's degree was accompanied with great pomp and display. The medical faculty and the graduating students, in full robe, marched in a procession to the church. There the degrees were awarded with lengthy ceremonies. Each physician received an especially engraved parchment, which allowed him to wear the fine robes of a physician, to demand fees for his services, and generally to live in noble fashion. All graduating physicians then had to swear aloud the Oath of Hippocrates:

"*. . . with purity and holiness I will pass my life and practice my art. I will not cut persons . . . but will leave this to be done by men who are practitioners of this work. Into whatever houses I enter, I will go into them for the benefit of the sick, and will abstain from every voluntary act of mischief and corruption . . . Whatever, in connection with my professional practice, I see or hear, in the life of men, which ought not to be spoken of abroad, I will not divulge . . . While I keep this Oath unviolated, may it be granted to me to* *enjoy life and the practice of the art, respected by all men, in all times! But should I trespass and violate this Oath, may the reverse be my fortune!"*

As the colorful crowd swarmed out into the bright afternoon sun, eyes blinking after the darkness of the church, Professor Leoniceno embraced Theo warmly.

"Congratulations, my boy! And now, have you thought of the future?"

"Why, no sir, I hadn't considered —"

"How would you like to stay on here at Ferrara and work with me? I am an old man with but a few years left. I should like to see a good man in my place —"

Just then, there was a commotion in the square. One of the university officials had come running and waving his hands. Now, puffing, gasping for breath, he was crying out some news to the people.

"What's going on?" Professor Leoniceno led Theo closer to the circle of men gathered about the official.

"A — great — victory!" gasped the man. "King of — France — Francis the First — victory over — Swiss troops —"

"Where? Where?" asked one of the crowd.

"Near Milan — fields of Marignano — over twenty thousand Swiss mercenaries slain — great battle —"

Someone hailed a wine seller passing by. The university official, with a sigh of thanks, drank deeply from the leather wine flask. He puffed out a deep breath of air, tossed the peddler a coin, and then proceeded to tell the story of the battle.

Francis I, the new King of France, had tested the strength of the Emperor Maximilian by invading the northern provinces

of Italy. About ten miles east of the city of Milan, the French troops had clashed with a force of twenty-five thousand Swiss mercenary soldiers, leased to the service of the emperor. Soldiering was a profession that knew no allegiance to any particular nation. The services of the professional soldier could be bought by any nobleman for some gold crowns. When two nations were at war, the noblemen and the mercenary soldiers did all the fighting. The citizens and peasants remained at home. Their fate might be death, imprisonment, slavery, or the paying of heavy fines, if their leaders lost.

The French troops had great numbers of a new and deadly weapon — the arquebus. This was a large hand gun, supported by a stick resting on the ground, and fired by a burning match held over a little hole filled with gunpowder. The explosion of the powder shot an iron bullet out with great speed. The swords and the iron pikes of the Swiss soldiers had been useless against the bullets fired by the French gunners. Men fell dead or wounded by the deadly iron hail. Then, when the Swiss ranks had become disorganized, the French foot soldiers had moved in with sword and lance to finish the job.

"Ferrara will no longer be safe for Swiss or Germans," cried one of the professors. "Those French barbarians will put us all to the sword."

"What will the emperor do now?" cried another.

Theo and Professor Leoniceno edged their way out of the crowd.

"Well, there's your answer, sir. It looks as though I'll have to leave Ferrara. I wish I could stay here with you. I have learned so much already."

"Perhaps the situation will change. Write to me often. I will let you know as soon as peace is restored."

There was little time to lose. In a few days, word came that the French troops were advancing rapidly from northern Italy. All the German and Swiss students and teachers prepared to leave Ferrara that day. There was only one road open — to the south.

Much as he wanted to remain in Ferrara, Theo was happy on the march again. It felt good to have the road under his boots, to see new places, different people, to lie in the shade of a tree listening to the birds. He was more used to traveling by foot than most of the university people who fled from Ferrara; in a few days, he had outdistanced them.

Again, he walked in the usual company of the road: beggars, peddlers, surgeons, quacks, and thieves. In the midst of such wanderers, he reached the city of Naples.

Naples, on the southeast coast of Italy, swarmed with the Spanish mercenary soldiers of the Hapsburg nobleman, Charles, Duke of Burgundy. This was the man soon destined to succeed Maximilian as the Emperor of the Holy Roman Empire. The display of Charles's military power in Naples was a counterfoil to the threat of the French king.

Theo stopped at a tavern to refresh himself. As he gave the innkeeper some coins for a dish of meat and a bottle of wine, he realized that he had little money left. He did not allow this discovery to spoil his appetite, and attacked the food vigorously.

At a table next to him, two men, clad in the Spanish fashion, with finely embroidered jerkins and the short, puffed-out pants called *haut-de-chausses,* talked so loudly he could not help overhearing.

"What if there is some real action? We would not have enough surgeons to attend to the wounded."

"Why not hire some, then? Are there no barber-surgeons in all of Naples?"

"Ah, it's not easy to get a skilled one to give up a good living for the army — and a foreign army, at that."

Though their conversation was in Spanish, Theo had understood. During his years at the universities and on the road, he had learned smatterings of most of the tongues spoken in Europe. He swallowed a last delicious morsel of meat, drained his glass, and walked over to their table.

"Do I understand that you gentlemen are looking for a surgeon?"

"And if we are?"

"Permit me to introduce myself — Theophrastus von Hohenheim, called Paracelsus, doctor of medicine from the University of Ferrara."

"And *you* want to be an army surgeon?"

"Gentlemen, I am not one of your physicians in fine velvet robes, hungry for gold pieces. I am interested in healing the sick. I am familiar with surgical techniques; in spite of the Hippocratic Oath, I have no scruples about using a scalpel. And I find myself a little embarrassed for spending money. Well?"

The Spaniards looked at each other. Was he sincere or a madman? Theo reassured them. "Gentlemen, I am a Swiss, and willing to serve the cause of the emperor. Despite my medical degree, I want to learn more about surgery."

An hour later, Theo found himself in the surgeon's quarters of the Spanish army, hired as an assistant surgeon. One of the men at the inn was the chief surgeon of the army. Ten minutes of conversation had convinced him of Theo's ability.

"We desperately need a man at one of the frontier villages where our troops have been skirmishing with marauders. There is a surgeon there, but he has more patients than he can handle. You can draw equipment and a horse from supply. I'll have one of our men escort you." The chief surgeon shook his hand. "Good fortune, Doctor Paracelsus!"

Ten hours later, Theo found himself in a large tent packed with men lying on litters. Some were groaning, some screaming; some lay pale and silent. Heads and limbs were wrapped in filthy bandages caked with blood. Dirt and vermin were everywhere.

The surgeon, José Avilla, was a slight, nervous Spaniard, with long mustachios. He smelled of garlic, and waved his hands wildly when he spoke. Theo introduced himself.

"Am I glad to see you, Paracelsus! This place is a madhouse. Each day patrols go out — each night, more wounded men. Have you ever tended a gunshot wound? Can you amputate a leg?"

"No — but I'll learn."

"Holy Host in Heaven, they send a neophyte into this pandemonium! Well, I have no time to teach you. You say you are a doctor? Well, here are cases no university physician ever saw."

An orderly rushed over to where they talked. "Sir, come at once! A new case — a lieutenant. Bad gunshot wound in the leg."

Avilla motioned Theo to follow him. "Here's your chance to begin learning."

On a litter next to the entrance of the tent lay a young Spanish officer. The orderly had already cut away the cloth of his hose. Avilla removed a makeshift bandage from the man's thigh. There was a gaping hole in the flesh, through which bits of bone could be seen in the clotted blood.

"Lucky man," said Theo, "missed the artery."

Avilla turned, a look of mild respect on his face. "Well, at least you are observant. Perhaps you will learn enough in time to be of use." He called to the orderly. "My apron, a scalpel, and a pair of tongs. Bring some towels, oil, and the

iron. I'll take the ball out here." And as the orderly ran off, he shouted after him, "Don't forget the wine!"

What followed seemed like a nightmare for Theo. Avilla tied a dirty, bloodstained leather apron about his waist, gulped a mouthful of wine from the bottle, and bent over the wound. "No point in wasting wine on an unconscious man," he muttered. With quick motions of the knife, he widened the wound. Then he roughly inserted the tongs and began to fish for the bullet.

The pain must have been intense. The wounded officer opened his eyes wide and began to scream like a frightened animal. Avilla paid no attention to the screams. With a cold expression on his face, he only dug deeper and deeper, until the points of the tongs struck metal. A moment later, he held the arquebus ball up in triumph. The lieutenant's screams changed to moans and he thrashed about on his litter.

"Give him some wine!" Avilla commanded the orderly, who had stooped to soak up the blood with a towel. "All right. Better, Lieutenant? Now we'll finish up, and you'll be as good as new."

He seized the iron, which was simply a small iron ring attached to a wooden handle. The ring had been heated red-hot. Avilla quickly plunged it into the wound. Theo could smell the burning flesh. The soldier, mercifully, had fainted.

Avilla pulled out the iron and motioned. The orderly poured boiling oil from a little caldron into the wound. The skin about the wound turned a fiery red. Then the orderly placed a little dried moss over the wound and tied a bandage about it. The lieutenant was carried off into the tent.

"Simple," pointed out the surgeon to Theo. "First, probe for the ball; second, cauterize; third, boiling oil and dressing."

"Do you always cauterize wounds?"

"Naturally. The gunpowder carried into the wound is poisonous. It must be burned out. And, as you probably know, the oil helps make pus."

"Ah, yes," muttered Theo sarcastically, "Galen again! The formation of pus is necessary to the healing of a wound. Señor Avilla, I will make a prediction. Tomorrow, that man's leg will be ready for amputation."

"So? It appears that you are not only a physician but a magician."

"Nevertheless, it is so."

Avilla sighed and threw up his hands. "Ah, I have no time for your fancies, Doctor Paracelsus. If you will be kind enough to assist me, there are a hundred men in there who require attention."

So ended Theo's first lesson in military surgery. There was little sleep for him that day. Under Avilla's direction, he moved among the wounded, bleeding a man here, suturing a ragged pike wound there. After a few hours, he already knew all the instruments of the army surgeon: the large saws for cutting through bone; the drills for trephining the skull; the speculi, or spoons, for pulling apart wounds; the different kinds of forceps for gripping arquebus balls, arrow barbs, or blood vessels; the various cautery irons shaped to fit all kinds of wounds.

At intervals, he returned to the side of the young lieutenant to examine the cauterized wound. The man's thigh was becoming bluish in color. He tossed and muttered feverishly on his litter. Theo noticed that his forehead was hot, his pulse rapid and fluttering.

"I change my prediction," he murmured to Avilla, as they passed each other in the tent. "Tomorrow, your fine lieutenant will be dead."

That night, more wounded came in. All wounded who could walk were evacuated from the tent to make room for the new ones. The discharged soldiers did not want to leave; they cursed the orderlies who sent them packing back to their quarters. However, they dared not disobey the chief surgeon's orders. Discipline was strong in the mercenary armies. The slightest infraction of orders was punished by flogging, or worse.

Theo was wakened from a deep sleep by a hand shaking him. He blinked his eyes open. It was morning. Avilla stood over his bed.

"Come, come, Doctor Paracelsus! We have no such luxuries as undisturbed sleep here. The bugle that blows reveille for the men blows the call for us, also."

When they entered the sick tent to inspect the wounded, they found the young lieutenant dead on his litter. Ten men had died in their sleep that night. Avilla gazed at Theo suspiciously, but said nothing. For Theo, the next few weeks were a blur of sick and wounded soldiers. He worked from dawn until dusk; sometimes, he and Avilla operated at night, in the flickering light of torches made of wood soaked in pitch.

The soldiers did not suffer only from battle wounds. There were petty complaints: stomach-aches, pounding heads from drinking too much wine, cuts and bruises from quarreling. More serious were the cases of camp fever, sometimes called the rashy fever, the wasting illness which either killed a man or left him unfit for military service. And there was that terrible new disease, the French sickness, that was ravaging the Spanish army. It was a strange and frightening disease that appeared in many forms. Strange sores would appear on a man's body; after a few weeks, they would disappear. A month or two later, he might suddenly find his skin overspread with pustular eruptions. His joints would begin to ache. Other victims simply developed a kind of brain fever and became raving madmen. In time, the body became emaciated and eaten away; death was inevitable. The disease was spreading throughout Italy, infecting people in the cities as well as the soldiers. It was rumored that the disease had appeared simultaneously with the advent of the French soldiers into Italy, hence the name. Strangely enough, the French soldiers, also infected with this sickness, called it the Neapolitan sickness.

Physicians did not know the cause of the disease. It was

thought that it was caused by the worms found in rotting meat. Most doctors felt that astrological events were behind the appearance of the French disease. Conflicting stars and planets had appeared in the same part of the sky at the same time. There were two methods used to fight the sickness. The first was the rubbing of pure quicksilver into the sores. Usually, the quicksilver was mixed into a greasy ointment, which was then applied. A newer method was the use of an exotic wood, guaiac wood, which was imported by the Spaniards from the New World. This wood was steeped in boiling water, and the infusion was drunk. The patient often sat in a little room with no ventilation, inhaling the smoke from a guaiac-wood fire.

Theo worked and sweated and learned. He said little but watched everything. He saw the effect of mercury on the cases of French disease. At first, the remedy seemed to work well. The rash would disappear for a while. But then the patients would develop strange symptoms. Saliva would begin to run from their mouths, and they could not control its flow. They developed convulsions and died. The guaiac treatment was too expensive to waste on a common soldier. In what few cases Theo saw treated with it, the wood seemed to do no good at all.

Theo began to work out methods of his own for the treatment of wounds. Unnoticed, almost surreptitiously, he "forgot" to cauterize the flesh, to use the boiling oil. Instead, he washed a wound carefully with clean water and bandaged it carefully with a clean dressing. In some of the gunpowder wounds, no pus developed. The bullet hole in the flesh began to fill in with a liquid that came from the body tissue itself. There was no smell of putrefaction, and no redness at the lips of the wound. These wounds healed in a short time.

The orderlies soon spread the tale. Avilla stormed into the tent where Theo had just removed the dressing from a soldier who had received a deep sword cut in the arm muscle.

"I hope you are ready to amputate that arm, Doctor Paracelsus!"

"Amputate? Why? This arm can be treated and saved. Look, the bone is only partially damaged. The flesh can be sewn together. Oh, perhaps this man will only have a limited use of the arm — still, that is better than no arm at all."

Señor Avilla's eyes flashed fire. "So these stories I hear about you are true! Instead of surgery, you are practicing some strange kind of medical tomfoolery. Look here, Paracelsus, my father was a surgeon, and his father before him. They handed down to me the knowledge and skills of a thousand years of surgery. What can you know about such things? I know the worth of the cautery iron and the oil. I know when a limb must be amputated. What you are trying to do goes against everything doctors and surgeons know and do."

Theo straightened up angrily. "Señor Avilla, I have eyes! I have watched men being maimed and killed here. You amputate without reason. You putrefy flesh instead of cleansing it. Do you know what your death rate is? Ten men a night — twenty men a night — what does that add up to in a month? You know much about surgery, I don't doubt that. But you know very little about healing. That isn't your fault — the men whose books you studied, your ancestors who trained you, also knew very little about healing." Theo pointed

to the wound. "Nature herself is a healer — we can only assist her! Pus in a wound is contrary to Nature. Her healing
fluids are pure and clean. Tearing and cutting the flesh to
remove a bullet only makes a wound worse, and keeps Nature from healing it."

Avilla waved Theo aside. "Let me remind you, Doctor
Paracelsus, that as long as you want to work for this army,
you are under my orders. We don't have time for fancy university theories here. Now either take that man's arm off or
leave this post. Those are my orders."

Theo looked at Avilla for a long moment. Then he untied
his surgeon's apron and flung it on the floor.

"I'm sorry," he said to the wounded soldier, "but he is
signing your death warrant. There is nothing I can do."

And while the hurt man and the orderlies watched, mouths agape, Theo turned and walked out of the hospital tent. An hour later, he was on the road again, walking toward the west and the beaches of the Mediterranean.

With the coming of darkness, he climbed a little hill at the edge of a lemon grove and prepared for sleep. As he stretched out on the ground, he saw the vast starry panorama of the sky spread above him. He knew the constellations intimately, their names and places, their significance in the interplay of heavenly and earthly forces.

Up there, above him, was the vast realm of God, the macrocosm, so great that no man could ever hope to comprehend it. And here he was, Paracelsus, a man, part of the microcosm, so small compared with the vastness that he was infinitesimal.

What knowledge that man has tells him anything about the external universe, the macrocosm? he asked himself. There were only three kinds he could think of: astronomy, natural philosophy, and theology. Astronomy dealt with the stars, philosophy with the tangible world, and theology with the realm of God.

What three things are important about man? he asked himself. His physical body, his feelings, and his soul. And these are the things with which medicine deals. An association began to form in his mind, hazy at first, but becoming clearer and clearer. The tiny world that is man must be understood through the great world that is God. Then, the three foundations of medicine must be astronomy, natural philosophy, and theology!

The full moon had risen, paling the stars into faint pinpoints of light. He sat up, pulled out writing materials, and began to put down these thoughts. Were these three enough? No, he had forgotten alchemy. There was a fourth foundation to medicine — the study of matter and its transformations. In the laboratory, new remedies for the illnesses of man could be discovered and perfected by man.

He threw the pen to the ground, exhausted by the words. "You call yourself Paracelsus," he said aloud, "and yet you cannot please a simpleton of an army surgeon! You treat men with quicksilver for the French sickness, and they die in agony! This morning you broke your Oath! You left a patient's side without treating him at all! The truth is, Theophrastus von Hohenheim, you are a nothing compared with Galen and Avicenna!"

Theo stood up, dispirited and sad. I should never have become a doctor, he said to himself, I shall never be what my father was. I don't even care about using my medical degree to become rich.

He was in an agony of doubt. "What are you, Doctor Paracelsus?" he cried aloud to the sky. "What are you?"

Once he had been so sure. But sometime during the past few weeks, Theo had lost himself. He no longer knew . . .

It came to him suddenly that perhaps the moon was his beacon light. Diana the Huntress, men called her. The golden orb hung in the western sky and gave him his answer. He would wander where the moon led; somewhere on man's earth, Paracelsus would find himself.

Quieted, he composed himself for sleep. His peace of mind lay in his very unrest. Already his brain was fomenting plans, ideas. If Galen did not know, if Avicenna did not know, who knew? To whom could he turn, where could he go, to find new remedies to heal the diseases of men?

One of the answers, he already knew — alchemy! The other came to him in a flash of inspiration: simplicity! What about the remedies that the simple folk, the peasants and the miners, used for their illnesses? These people never went to professional physicians. Yet the simple folk often knew how to cure themselves by using remedies handed down by word of mouth from generation to generation. What herbs did they know about that Galen never knew?

He began to see something of his goal. First, to seek out all that the common people knew about curing sickness; secondly, to use alchemy to probe the herbs, to discover the matter within them that effected the cure. He would roam the earth until he found a way to heal every sickness that plagued mankind.

Chapter Five

FOR THE NEXT EIGHT YEARS, Theophrastus Paracelsus von Hohenheim wandered over most of the civilized world. He traveled on foot, by horse, in coaches, in ships, and on sleds. He shivered in the bleak, frozen tundras of Lapland and sweated in the hot, lush reaches of the Nile. He earned his bread as military surgeon, alchemist's assistant, miner, and visiting scientist. He talked to thousands of people and filled his knapsacks with notes on medicine, alchemy, and astronomy. He talked to professors, noblemen, peasants, miners, priests, in fact to everyone he met.

From the Italian coast, he was ferried to the island of Sicily by fishermen. There, from the harbor of Catania, he saw the smoking crater of Mount Etna. Another boat brought him north to the great seaport of Genoa; he did not tarry long in the bustling, dirty city, but headed east for France. From some of the doctors at Ferrara, he had heard about the famous University of Montpellier on the southern coast of France. Here, in medieval times, had been the greatest school of medicine and pharmacy. Perhaps he would discover what he sought there!

But at Montpellier the professors talked only of Avicenna. The apothecary shops were filthy with rats and vermin. Their pharmacy was the old medieval pharmacy, full of recipes calling for the stewed remains of toads, mice, vipers, and other unsavory items. "These pharmacists live in filth," wrote Theo in his notes. "They know nothing of alchemy. Their medicines are composed of sorcery mixed with ignorance."

Dissatisfied, he followed the seacoast west to Spain. In the port city of Cartagena, he discovered an army being assembled. The Spanish government had declared war on the Sultan of Algiers. Theo signed up as military surgeon. A week later, he found himself on a troop carrier, part of a great fleet of warships, bound for Oran, a Spanish port in North Africa.

The Spanish campaign against the Berbers of Algiers was short, swift, but bloody. The soldiers of the sultan gave no quarter and asked for none. Theo found himself once again in the midst of the blood and horror of the medical tents. His fingers became more skilled; he handled the scalpel with assurance. The bone saw, in his hands, became a surgical instrument, not a carpenter's tool.

With the capture of the sultan, the war ended. Back in Spain, with a fuller purse, Theo wandered aimlessly to the north. In the city of Salamanca, he worked for a while in the laboratory of an alchemist. There he learned some of the alchemical secrets handed down by the famous medieval alchemist, Raymond Lully. Two hundred years before, Lully had introduced the study of Oriental languages at the University of Salamanca. From Salamanca, Theo walked to Valladolid. He was shown the grave of the brave Italian sailor, Christopher Columbus, the first man to dare the terrors of an unknown ocean. From Valladolid, Theo went north to the port of Lisbon in Portugal.

In this year, 1518, Lisbon boiled with excitement. It was as though a fever had swept through the city, infecting all it touched with a lust for adventure, for exploration, for promised riches. From Lisbon, tall-masted caravels sailed to the New World beyond the western horizon. From Lisbon, government ships departed for the new Portuguese colonies in Asia and Africa. In the streets of Lisbon one could meet Indians from Calcutta and Indians from the New World.

But this was not the kind of excitement Theo sought. He spoke to physicians, to pharmacists, to alchemists. He poked about in some of the hospitals staffed by members of the religious orders. There was nothing new and exciting in medicine to be found in Lisbon. Theo turned his face to the northeast and moved across the Pyrenees, back into France. By the end of 1518, he was in the city of Paris.

Paris was a city of extremes. There were beautiful palaces of marble and filthy huts. Elegantly dressed ladies stepped daintily from their carriages, assisted by long-haired page boys. Gawking at the gold filigree of their silken gowns were the poor people of Paris: toothless hags clutching their dirty ragged clothing close to their withered bodies; little children with muck on their faces and vermin in their hair, and gaunt hunger in their eyes.

The University of Paris was one of the greatest universities

111

in the world. Most of the German universities had patterned themselves after Paris. Theo came to the professors at the medical school with an open mind. He spoke to them about his basic pillars of medicine, of the new remedies to be found for disease in alchemy.

To his disgust, he found that the wandering scholar, Fleury, had been right. The medical school at Paris was still rockbound in the past. Galen was their master; the old remedies, based on the humor theory, were their prescriptions. He offered to demonstrate for them a new salve he had invented at Salamanca for the cure of leg ulcers.

"This comes from the alchemy of nature," he told the dourfaced university physicians. "It contains a poison so powerful that it must be used only in tiny doses. Too much, and the flesh is burned away."

"If you are any kind of doctor," put in another, "then you know that opposite cures opposite. Diseases are caused by poisons. They must be cured by nonpoisons."

"You are wrong," declared Theo. "Poisons *can* cure poisons. *Like cures like* — that is my motto. The important thing is to experiment, to discover the proper dosage for the specific condition."

The doctors of Paris laughed at this strange man who called himself Paracelsus. But he still defied them. "Give me your most difficult skin ulcer," he dared them, "and I will heal it."

With the air of leading a clown to the circus, they took Theo to a hospital. There in one of the beds lay a poor wretch with a large, foul hole in his calf. The lesion was purplish and filled with pus.

"Here is a cancer that is obviously incurable. Try your poison."

Theo examined the ulcer. He took the man's pulse, looked at the whites of his eyes, and listened to the beating of his heart. He noted the many little cuts in the skin; apparently bleeding had been the chief treatment.

"Give me ten days," he said, "and you will have a whole leg." The doctors departed, smiling and winking among themselves.

Theo called in the Sister who served as nurse and asked that a pallet be brought so that he could sleep in the room. Her eyes widened. This was strange conduct for a doctor!

"What have you been feeding this patient?" he asked when she returned with a sack filled with straw.

"Gruel, Doctor."

"Nothing else?"

"No, sir. Those were the orders."

Theo exploded. "Good Lord! Look at his cheekbones! Look at his ribs! That man is starving to death. No wonder the ulcer won't heal." He ordered a diet of meat, milk, and fresh fruit. He also asked for hot water and clean dressings.

Theo carefully washed the ulcer and cleared away the dead flesh from the edges. He applied some of his salve to the wound and bandaged it. When the food came, the patient wolved it like a starving animal. "Slowly, slowly, friend," smiled Theo, "you will be well fed from now on."

For nine nights, Theo slept in the same room as his patient. Every day, he unwrapped the bandages from the ulcer, washed it, and applied the ointment. On the second morning, a barber-surgeon walked in brusquely and, without a word, began to prepare the patient for bleeding. Theo seized the astonished man by the scruff of the neck and threw him out.

On the morning of the tenth day, the Parisian professors came to the hospital. When they walked into the room, Theo was in the act of unwrapping the bandage from his patient's leg.

"Well, Doctor Paracelsus?" They spoke in the gentle tones one uses when humoring a madman.

"Here you are, gentlemen. Not quite perfectly healed, but I think it is well on the way." Theo gently removed the last fold of linen. The purplish hole was gone. Instead, there was an area of new pink tissue growing in. The patient's face was radiant with health. The university doctors looked at one another. Without a word, they left the hospital.

The news of the miraculous cancer cure spread quickly.

When Theo left the hospital, he was followed by curious crowds. Every ten feet, someone stopped him to beg his attendance at a sickbed. The name *Doctor Paracelsus* was buzzed throughout the city of Paris, and to it was added the word *magician*.

For the university doctors of Paris, the curing of the ulcer was a bitter pill. They determined to revenge themselves on Paracelsus. A whispering campaign was begun, slandering him as a traveling quack. He was called a charlatan, a fool, and a crazy man who dared to oppose all that was holy in medicine.

Theo laughed at their stupidity and turned his back on Paris. "The doctors at the Sorbonne," he wrote, "think that their stiff necks and their wisdom reach up into Heaven. Their medicine is false and stupid. They have never heard of experimenting, nor do they understand the connection between experience and theory."

From Paris, he drove himself relentlessly, always on the move, always seeking, always asking. A lull in the habitual squabbles between England and France gave him an opportunity to cross the choppy waters of the Thames River. He was jostled by the crowds as he peered into the shops on London Bridge. He watched a condemned criminal being beheaded in the square before the Tower of London, and saw the head stuck on a pike and lifted high for the benefit of the crowd. He was almost pressed flat in the mob that turned out to watch their king, Henry the Eighth, and his wife, Catherine of Aragon, ride from their palace to Westminster Abbey.

From London, he headed west toward the Cornwall coast. A fishing smack carried him across the Irish Sea to that strange country where the people were fiercely proud and chafed

115

under the English rule. He found the Irish peasants devout and very superstitious. Their talk was full of stories about the "little people," the leprechauns of the forest. Theo listened to their tales with deep interest. He recalled the stories of the miners who had seen the kobolds in the depths of the earth. And he remembered only too well that terrible day at Villach when the miner George had seen the kobold — just before the explosion in the lower level.

He recrossed the Irish Sea further north into the country of Scotland. Here was a wild and beautiful country, whose major cities, Glasgow and Edinburgh, were cultural centers. But Theo found little to interest him there. He turned southward toward the continent of Europe again. A month later, he was in Belgium, heading northeast to the Low Countries, the Netherlands. He arrived at the city of Antwerp to find it teeming with people. It was the time of the great Antwerp Fair.

This was one of the gayest annual holidays in Europe. Merchants came from every country to display their wares. Farmers came with great loads of fruit and vegetables. They drove their best hogs and cows to Antwerp to sell them to the highest bidders. Brightly colored tents filled the fairground. Peddlers hawked their wares in a thousand different chants. Children dodged in and out of the crowd, eluding the restraining hands of their parents. Laughter and music filled the air. There was singing and dancing, and the smell of roasting meats from the barbecue pits.

Theo loved this wonderful little country, where the streets were mostly water-filled canals, and four-armed windmills ground all the grain. But most of all, he loved the fair. He loved mingling with the people, to look at their faces. He made it a point to speak to many peasants, particularly the old women. He had the knack of getting around the suspicious attitude which most peasants had toward strangers.

"Now, auntie," he would wheedle an old crone, "tell us what you'd be doing for an aching knee. Everyone knows that women are wiser in these matters."

"Hee-hee! Young man, stop your coaxing! I'm too old for your flattery! But my grandmother used to say:

> *"If a swollen joint keeps you in bed,*
> *Then take a piece of flannel red;*
> *Dye it over full times nine —*
> *Place it on, and all is fine!"*

And Theo would carefully copy all he learned from the peasants into his notes. He knew that much of what he wrote was not true. But he felt that in time he would sift the truth out of all the knowledge he had accumulated.

"There is more to be learned at the Antwerp Fair," he wrote, "than in all the universities of Germany."

He bade Antwerp farewell and moved on to the east, along the coast of the North Sea. Here, in a long row from Germany to Russia stretched the cities of the Hansa, the organized league of merchant traders. The Hansa had grown, in three hundred years, from a handful of seaport towns to a well-knit, strongly armed group of cities. The loyalty of these cities cut across national boundaries; the men of the Hansa were loyal to their business only. Together, they attacked and cut down any enemy that threatened the trade their ships enjoyed with all the countries of the world.

Theo saw the magnificent Hansa cities of Bremen and Hamburg. Their harbors were crowded with tall-masted ships. Their docks teemed with workers unloading furs from Lapland, minerals from Sweden, and cloth from England. Further east were the Hansa cities of Lübeck, Wismar, and Rostock. Theo noticed that the Hansa cities lacked the cosmopolitan atmosphere he had found in Lisbon. Most of the trade was confined to the countries that bordered the Baltic Sea — Germany, Poland, Russia, and the Scandinavian countries. The chief export seemed to be fish. And from the grumbling of the sailors and the merchants, Theo understood that the competition of the English and Dutch shipping had begun to make inroads on the Hansa trade.

Theo sailed from Rostock across the island-studded corner of the east Baltic Sea to Copenhagen, capital city of Denmark. Here a chance to earn some money and to improve his surgical skill awaited him. Christian II, the cruel ruler of Denmark, had assembled an army to conquer Sweden, his neighbor to the north. The King of the Netherlands had sent soldiers to help Christian, in return for a favor: the Hansa harbors of Norway were to be opened to trade with the Netherlands.

Good army surgeons were hard to find. Theo had no difficulty getting the job. In a few weeks, he sailed with the first Danish troops across the narrow strip of sea between Copenhagen and Sweden. The campaign was brief. The Swedish troops were easily overpowered by the superior numbers of invaders, and King Gustavus of Sweden was captured. Theo had little work to do.

However, his work did not go unnoticed. Someone whispered in King Christian's ear about a fine surgeon named

Doctor Paracelsus, who had shown a skill beyond compare in treating wounded soldiers. The king did not forget. When he came, in victory, to the Swedish capital of Stockholm to be crowned King of Sweden, Christian ordered that this Doctor Paracelsus be raised to the position of "Physician Ordinary to the King." There was a little ceremony, during which Theo knelt before King Christian and had a golden chain hung about his neck.

Now, beginning in 1520, life itself seemed golden to Theo. He was given the specific duty of reorganizing the apothecary shops of Denmark. Here was a chance to put his new ideas about medicines to work.

Somehow, he never found the time to return to Copenhagen for this task. Sweden was too exciting a country. As the king's physician, Theo could commandeer vehicles for traveling anywhere he wished. He spent months making trips up into the northern parts of the country, visiting the famous copper mines at Falun, and the new university in the city of Upsala. He saw the bleak snow tundras of the far north, where the sun shone both day and night. He rode among the strange inhabitants of Lapland, the people who dressed in furs and lived on fish. They bred a small antlered animal called a reindeer, and used it for meat, milk, and to pull their sleds. From their medicine men, or shamans, he learned about many new herbs and plants. Full of wonder at the strange sights he had witnessed, he came back to Stockholm in the autumn of 1520.

He returned to a city struck by a holocaust. The Swedes had risen in revolt against Christian. The cruel Danish monarch had lured ninety of the highest noblemen in Stockholm to a feast and had ordered them to be executed at the banquet table. Aroused by this "blood bath," noblemen and serfs alike rose in arms against the Danish invaders.

Theo did not wish to be trapped in this struggle. From what he heard, he knew that the Danish occupation of Sweden was doomed. After bribing a sea captain, he slipped out of Stockholm one night on a Hansa boat. He took with him only his notes, the gold chain of his office, and a great sword of forged steel, which he had purchased from a Swedish nobleman. He named the sword Azoth, the secret alchemical name for Mercury.

The boat carried him across the Baltic to the land of the Order of Teutonic Knights. This was Prussia. The knights were an old order of church warriors, dedicated to keeping the heathen of the east from crossing the borders of Christian lands.

In the river port of Stettin, Theo discovered that the Teutonic Knights were organizing to march against the city of Danzig, a coastal city that had defied their rule. He remembered that his grandfather, George von Hohenheim, had once been a commander in the order. Theo sought out the headquarters of the knights in Stettin.

Mere mention of the name von Hohenheim worked magic. Theo was welcomed and thumped on the back by the grizzled old warriors who remembered his grandfather well.

"And you are his grandson! And a doctor, too! Think of that, George's grandson a doctor!"

"And a good surgeon, too," added Theo proudly.

A surgeon? The knights put their heads together and agreed that the order could always use a good surgeon during a campaign. Theo was hired immediately, and at a good salary, to accompany them in the attack upon Danzig.

Off to the east he rode, now on his own splendid horse, in the company of the officers of the order. During the march, he treated the sick soldiers with a skill that made the Teuton warriors shake their heads and look at him with awe in their faces.

A few weeks later, the walls of Danzig appeared on the horizon. The Teuton army maneuvered into position for an assault. The heavy cannon and catapults were trained on the walls. Ladders were readied for climbing. Arquebuses were cleaned and oiled; swords and lances were sharpened. Bowmen tested their strings and checked their arrows for warping. The order was given. Amid the crashing of the cannon and the barking of the smaller firearms, the Teutonic Knights made for the walls of Danzig. With frightful shouting, they raised their scaling ladders. Parts of the walls were burning from the Greek fireballs that had been hurled out by the catapults. The citizens of Danzig scrambled about with pails of water, trying to put the fires out. With long poles, they pushed the ladders filled with climbing knights back onto the ground.

And the walls held. The attack failed, not once, but many times. Theo and his fellow surgeons worked without rest. The sick tent was packed with injured and dying men. There was no time for sentiment or kindness. Those who could manage to walk had their wounds dressed and were dismissed. Those who were obviously dying were dragged from the pallets to make room for the new wounded. The commanders of the knights knew that taking the city of Danzig would not be a

simple matter. They settled down for a siege, hoping to starve the city into submission.

It was November. The cold bleakness of winter began to settle on the plains before Danzig. The men of the Teuton army began to grumble about the weather. Their leaders had expected a second army under Sir Albrecht, Grand Master of the Teutonic Knights, to join them. But the supporting army never came; Albrecht was fighting off another Polish army elsewhere. Sadly, the order was given to retreat. Horses were hitched up to the cannon and the catapults. The Teutonic Knights turned their faces toward Prussia, while the citizens of Danzig cheered and howled at them from the parapets.

But Theo did not go with the retreating army. He was tired of blood and war, of bullet holes and flesh slashed into ribbons by sword thrusts. He turned his horse east and rode away from

the knights. He knew there was little danger for him. He did not wear their armor, and a wandering surgeon was welcome almost anywhere.

To the east of Danzig lay the important city of Koenigsberg. The Poles had just captured it from the Teutonic Knights, and Theo found everyone in the city rejoicing over the victory. He learned that the Poles were a proud people, who had suffered on one side from the heavy hand of the Teutonic Knights, and on the other, from the attacks of the Russians and Tartars.

There was momentary peace at this time with Russia, however. This huge country, which covered a large part of eastern Europe, was a land of mystery for most western Europeans. Actually, more was known about the habits of the Indians in the New World than about those of the Russians. They were said to be barbarous, cannibals, more than seven feet tall, and two-headed. It was in Koenigsberg that Theo met his first Russian, and found these stories to be untrue.

A public notice had been posted that an ambassador from the court of Grand Prince Basil the Third in Moscow had come to Koenigsberg to invite men of learning to visit Russia. The Russian monarch planned to make Moscow the great cultural center of eastern Europe. Scholars who accepted would be treated like noblemen. They would be furnished transportation to Moscow; there, they would be lodged in lavish dwellings near the court; also, their food and lodging would be supplied free, in addition to a handsome monthly stipend.

Theo could not resist the lure of a new country, new people, new adventure. He sought out the Russian ambassador, a tall, bearded man, dressed in a long velvet cloak trimmed with ermine fur. After a brief Latin conversation, Theo was accepted as a guest of the Russian government. He could leave, the ambassador pointed out, that very afternoon, if he wished, with some other guests. With a flourish, Theo signed the contract of his stay *Doctor Paracelsus*.

Between Koenigsberg and Moscow there stretched the longest seven hundred miles in Theo's memory. Over the frozen snow flew the sleds. There was little to see but snow, trees, and the horizon retreating relentlessly before them. They stopped only at military relay stations to change horses and to bolt some food. Occasionally the sleighs were followed by wolf packs, gray doglike animals whose open panting mouths showed rows of sharp teeth. Some of the scholars, who had never seen any wild animals, were frightened by the sight of the red, lolling tongues of the wolves. But the Russian

124

drivers only laughed and flicked their whips in the faces of the most daring leaders of the packs. At night, the howling of the wolves could be heard for miles.

Through forests, past cities, over wide rivers frozen solid, they rode for two months. One morning, the leading sled stopped short. The driver waved his arms and pointed. There, a distant sparkle in the sun, were the towers of Moscow. Theo, with the rest, was stirred by an intense excitement.

As they approached, Theo could see that the walls of Moscow were high and formidable. Back of the walls were a group of towers, built in the style of Italian campaniles. This was the palace called the Kremlin, home of the Grand Prince Basil.

The gates of Moscow opened wide to receive them. The sleighs entered amid a loud ringing of cathedral bells. Inside the city walls, a special escort from the palace awaited them. The Russian soldiers were dressed in heavy quilted jackets and fur hats. They rode small, spirited horses, from whose mouths and nostrils vapor poured into the freezing air. Down the snow-packed street they led the newcomers, between two rows of staring, silent people. When the party reached the steps of the Kremlin, the escorts dismounted. Looking up, Theo could see the golden-domed towers topped by crosses symbolic of the Eastern Orthodox Church. The Russian people were members of this Church, which had broken away from the Roman Catholic Church almost four hundred years before.

Theo found Grand Prince Basil to be a vain and crafty man. Strangely enough, he seemed to be suspicious of the very foreigners he had invited to his kingdom. He and his noble-

125

men, the boyars, lived in extravagant splendor. Their clothing was encrusted with gold and jewels. They looked with disdain upon the scholarly visitors.

As for the common people of Russia, Theo found them in a woeful state of ignorance. There was no medical profession; sick persons depended upon superstition and witchcraft for healing. Many of the poor lived like animals. Even among the wealthy noblemen, Theo found a strain of savagery. A man could be slain on the spot for an ill-timed word.

Theo was assigned to a nobleman's house in one of the suburbs of Moscow. Here, he lived in an atmosphere of distrust. Not only was he a foreigner, but to the household he was not a true Christian. His host washed his hands clean of taint after shaking Theo's hand. At mealtime, Theo had a separate set of dishes and a chair set apart at the table.

But Theo had a winning way with him that conquered his

suspicious hosts. After a few weeks, he had learned enough Russian to be able to speak to them. And after he had cured one of the babies of a bad fever, they began to accept him.

Theo knew that there was little to be learned about medicine in Moscow. He was enchanted, however, with being in a different land, among new people. His host took him on long rides into the country in a sleigh called a troika. It was fun to go dashing along the white fields with the snow blowing off the horses' hoofs into their faces.

On one of these troika rides, they ventured further out than ever before into the great plain of the Volga, the wide river that ran past Moscow. Theo had his knapsack of notebooks with him; he never let them out of his sight. He was enjoying the majestic sweep of the horizon all about the flat earth. Suddenly, the sleigh driver screamed and pointed. Coming toward them at a gallop from the rear was a large band of mounted men.

The nobleman twisted in his seat to look. His face turned white. "We are lost," he muttered to Theo. "They are Tartars!"

Theo had heard of the fierce Tartars. Once, the ancestors of these slant-eyed raiders had ruled all of Asia. In the year 1224, under the leadership of Genghis Khan, the Tartars had swept into Russia and had conquered the land from the Baltic to the Black Sea. In the south, they even advanced into Turkey and captured Constantinople. For over two hundred years, the Tartars had ruled this vast area. But now they had fallen upon evil days. The Russians had banded together and had broken the Tartar rule. The Turks had recaptured Constantinople. The Tartars lived on the outskirts of Russia in little nomadic bands. Like dogs worrying a piece of meat, they made swift

127

raids into the settled districts of the cities, carrying away prisoners and loot. Most of their prisoners were sold to the Turks into slavery.

"I have this!" Theo patted the great sword Azoth, buckled to his side.

Fear widened the Russian's eyes. "No! No! Do not offer resistance! That means certain death."

Howling, the Tartars swooped down upon the sleigh and surrounded it. They seized the bridles of the horses and forced them to a halt. Theo saw that they were short men, with dark-skinned faces and slanted eyes. They spoke among themselves in a strange language. One of the Tartars motioned the driver to get down. The poor man was frozen with fear; he could not move. With an exclamation of impatience, the Tartar ran his sword through him, and pushed him, dying, to the ground. The others laughed. Theo and the Russian did not dare move.

One Tartar, who appeared to be the leader, approached them. He pointed to Theo's sword with a meaningful gesture. Theo unbuckled the belt and let his beloved Azoth fall to the ground. The Tartar jumped from his horse and picked up the sword. He gave an order in Russian. The nobleman held out his hands and let the jeweled rings be torn from them. The Tartar grinned wickedly and spoke again. The nobleman translated for Theo. "He says that they will trade us for soap."

The Tartar camp was a day's gallop away from the spot where the troika had been stopped. It was already night when they came to the fifty low, flat-topped tents huddled together, sides billowing in the wind that swept across the plains. Smoke came from holes in the roofs; the Tartar women were cooking supper for their men.

Theo and the Russian, hands tied behind them, were pushed rudely from the sleigh toward the largest tent. Inside, they were forced to their knees before a rude throne. In the flickering light of torches held by guards, Theo saw the leader of the Tartars sitting there, a squat man wearing a peaked iron helmet and a silver breastplate.

"One of the sub-khans — a ruler of this region," whispered the nobleman.

The khan pointed to Theo. He spoke Russian well, and Theo could understand. "Who is this man? He does not resemble the men of Moscow."

"He is the guest of His Majesty, the Grand Prince —" began the nobleman.

A wicked gleam came into the Tartar's eye. "Ah, then perhaps he is worth a good ransom, eh?"

Theo rose to his feet. "Your Excellency, I can speak for myself," he began. A guard moved to thrust him down, but the khan waved the man away.

"Speak, then."

"Better hold this Russian nobleman for ransom. As for me, my name is Paracelsus. I am a physician, a healer of great repute in my country. The Grand Prince will not give you the tenth of an ounce of gold for me. But I am worth more to you than to him. I can teach your doctors ways of healing which they have never known."

A look of amazement appeared on the khan's face. The Tartars admired courage. Their eastern heritage had taught

them to admire wisdom. He leaned toward a guard. "Bring our healer of the sick here."

A moment later, an old man with a short white beard was led into the tent. He bowed to the khan and asked his wish.

"This man says he is a healer of the sick. Can you test him?"

Before the old man could speak, Theo turned toward him. In the army he had learned that the best defense was a swift attack. "If you are truly a physician, sir," he said, "then you will understand this." And word for word, in Latin, he recited the entire Oath of Hippocrates.

The doctor listened carefully and turned to the khan when Theo had finished. "Sire, he speaks a certain oath taken by doctors of the west. Once, when I was in the land of the Turks, I heard of this. If he can say this, he is truly a physician." He spoke to Theo. "How would you treat a wound of the sword in the arm?"

Theo explained how it was the custom of western surgeons to cauterize the wound and to pour boiling oil on it, but that he, Paracelsus, abstained from such horror. He described his method of stopping the bleeding and cleansing the wound. He spoke of his belief in nature and its powers of healing tissue.

When he had finished, the Tartar doctor remained silent for a moment. Then he walked over to Theo and took his hand. "Exalted one, this man is indeed a wonderful healer of the sick. I am an old man, and have heard many things. But tonight I have heard the greatest wisdom of all!"

The khan rose. "Very well. This man who calls himself Paracelsus may remain with us as our honored guest."

For six months, Theo remained with the Tartars. He learned that they were Mohammedans; they believed that Allah was the true God. Death meant little to them; did not their prophet, Mohammed, promise them a more rewarding life in Heaven? Theo learned to like their food, hot with spices and ginger.

From the old doctor, he learned many of the mysteries of eastern medicine. Though much of their medicine was connected with sorcery and magic, Theo found many of their healing methods to be successful. The Tartar showed him the different kinds of plants which he pressed, boiled, or stewed in order to obtain their active ingredients. One of the most impressive Tartar remedies was a mixture of herb juices which could stop pain or cause sleep, depending upon the dosage taken. Its action was more subtle and longer than any drug he had seen in the west. Theo called the mixture of herb juices laudanum.

131

"I can only sing its praises," he told the Tartar physician, "and the Latin for 'praises' is *laudes*."

The days flowed into weeks. Theo watched the Tartar horsemen go and return from their raids on the Russian cities. He helped the old doctor treat the sick and wounded. But he began to feel again the urge to be on the move, to search elsewhere for a greater understanding of nature. Was he to be a prisoner of the Tartars for the rest of his life?

Hesitantly, Theo spoke of his desire to the Tartar physician. The old man only smiled and brought him before the khan. "Tell the great khan your wishes, Doctor Paracelsus."

The khan listened gravely, without a word. When Theo had finished, he said simply, "Good doctor, we are not altogether barbarians. In our lands, wise men are respected. They are free to go where they will. You have given us freely of your wisdom. If it is Allah's will that you must go elsewhere to find greater wisdom, so be it!"

He motioned to a guardsman. "Arrange an escort for Doctor Paracelsus." Turning to Theo, he added, "It will be safest to travel south, through the country called the Ukraine, along the shores of the Black Sea."

A few weeks later, Theo found himself waving farewell to the Tartar soldiers who had ridden with him to the borders of the Ukraine. He had with him his great sword, Azoth, his notebooks, food, and a large stock of laudanum. He sat on the back of a shaggy Tartar pony, a gift from the khan. With a last flourish, Theo turned the pony's head to the west and galloped away.

Across the flat black earth of the Ukraine lay his path to the west. He rode across the Polish border and then swerved south to follow the traders' routes, through Hungary, then west again until he reached the Danube River. There, he sold his Tartar pony and paid a boatman to ferry him upstream through the country of Croatia. To the northeast, across the Adriatic Sea, lay Venice, the fabulous Italian city whose streets were canals of water.

Theo reached the east coast of the Adriatic and wandered north on foot. He reveled in the joys of the open road, in the companionship of his fellow travelers, monk and peddler, peasant and merchant, rogue and scholar. Here and there, he stopped to treat an ailment, receiving as payment a fine dinner or fresh clothing. At length, he arrived at the famous mines in the province of Idria. These mines belonged to the Venetians. From them came the purest quicksilver to be found in all Europe.

Theo signed on as a miner. He did not need the wages, nor was he interested in the art of mining quicksilver. But he watched carefully the men beside whom he worked, noting the eyes, the breathing, the color of the skin. He learned quickly to discern the symptoms of mercurial poisoning. Had he not seen enough of that while he was treating the French disease? He filled his notebooks with descriptions of the diseases of miners. Theo remembered his boy's promise to the miner George in Villach: when I am a doctor, I shall find a way to heal all miners.

When he had seen enough, he left the mines as quietly as he had come. From Idria to Venice was a short journey. Theo found the city in a furor of military recruiting. The struggle between Charles V, the Holy Roman Emperor, and Francis, King of France, had heightened. The Venetians had decided

133

to throw their lot in with Francis, and were raising a mercenary army to send to his aid. In this same year, Suleiman, Sultan of the Turks and ruler of the Ottoman Empire, had sent
a great navy to capture the island of Rhodes.

But Theo was tired of war. He sought only an escape from
Venice to places where he had never been. With relief, he
found a sea captain who offered to take him to the island of
Crete in the Mediterranean Sea. From there, the ship would
be going on to Egypt, to pick up a cargo at Alexandria.

From the deck, Theo watched the marble palaces of Venice
fade into the mist of the Adriatic shore. He had been wandering over the face of the earth for six years. In his knapsack
lay books in which was scribbled much of what human beings
knew or believed about nature. But there were many empty
pages left that would have to be filled before Doctor Paracelsus would be able to solve the great mysteries of the human
body.

Chapter Six

THE LIGHTHOUSE OF ALEXANDRIA, one of the seven wonders of the world, had been destroyed by an earthquake almost three hundred years before Theo sailed into the harbor. But he was shown a pile of stone on the little island of Pharos. This rubble marked the remains of the huge beacon that had lighted the way for ships from every corner of the civilized world.

Alexandria itself, now under the control of the Turks, scarcely resembled the great seaport it had once been. The value of the city as a jumping-off point to the countries of the east had dwindled with the discovery of a sea route about the Cape of Good Hope by the Portuguese voyager, Vasco da Gama. Theo found the people of Alexandria to be a cosmopolitan mixture of many nationalities. Greek, Jew, Arab, and Egyptian lived side by side in this city of stone mansions and mud huts.

Theo was anxious to see more of the wonders of this ancient land. The Nile River itself was a strange quirk of nature. For thousands of miles, its waters gave birth to a lush, fertile valley between lifeless deserts of burning sand. Every year, the river overflowed its banks. Where the waters receded, the enriched topsoil would grow fine grain. The Nile River had dominated Egyptian life and thought for thousands of years.

Theo had no trouble obtaining passage on a boat bound for the city of Cairo, just down the river from Alexandria. At Cairo, he suffered a native guide to mount him on the back of a camel. Bobbing up and down on the hump of this strange beast, Theo rode off to see the great pyramid of the Pharaoh Cheops at Giza.

The little sailboat in which Theo sat moved slowly down the Nile beyond Cairo. The days grew hotter. Often, the banks were quite hidden by large clumps of papyrus reeds, the same plant which had served as a source of writing paper for the scribes of ancient Egypt. Flocks of birds rose in flight, as they passed. Theo had seen pelicans, and was amused by the way they dived into the water after fish. But he was unprepared for the breath-taking beauty of the bird called the ibis. These cranes rose from the water in graceful flight, beating the air with long white wings. On the shore, the naked-necked vultures sat, their baleful eyes watching for a sign of death.

A month later, the boat dropped anchor at the ancient city of Thebes. Theo had seen many wonders along the way. Herds of huge animals had risen from the waters to stare at the little sailboat. These were the monsters called hippopotamus — a combination of Greek words that meant "river horse." The hippos shook their heads and opened their vast mouths wide

to show stumps of ivory teeth. From the banks of the river, great scaly lizards slithered into the water with a splash. These were crocodiles, the most dangerous of the river animals. The sight of their long mouths filled with rows of sharp teeth sent chills down Theo's back.

"The monsters of the Nile," he wrote in his books, "are enough to make you want to run for the protection of your mother's apron."

At Thebes he found the ruins of many ancient temples, their walls covered with the beautiful picture writing of the ancient Egyptians. Theo found an old priest who was able to translate the writings — called hieroglyphics — for him. There were the usual stories of great gods and their power over men and kings. On one wall, Theo discovered a group of hieroglyphics which seemed familiar.

"Ah, yes," the old man said, "this is a story of the doctors of the old times. Here, you see, they are performing an operation. They are removing the top of a man's head to heal an injury."

Theo was fascinated. "These ancient doctors were master surgeons!"

"Yes. The story here tells of many wonderful healings that were performed by them." And the priest translated, while Theo wrote feverishly in his notebook.

He would have stayed longer at Thebes, but the heat became oppressive. He learned that a little further up the Nile, at a place called Assuan, he would be able to follow the caravan route to the Red Sea. Here was Theo's chance to see the land of the Bible.

Again he bobbed for days on the hump of a swaying camel and found respite on the deck of a boat moving over the calm waters of the Red Sea. From Akaba to Jerusalem, he walked, viewing with interest old Roman ruins and sites of Biblical events which he had read about often. Finally, he came to the seaport of Acre and gazed up at the stone walls which had been besieged and finally taken by King Richard the Lionhearted of England. Theo was filled with a strong sense of emotion. This was the land that was so dear to the tradition of his religion. Seeing it with his own eyes made him feel closer than ever to that tradition.

In Acre, however, he heard mutterings about the island of Rhodes. The Knights of Saint John were still holding out, but it was becoming more and more difficult to stave off the attacks of the Turks. They needed food, they needed ammunition — they needed doctors. Theo felt that it was his duty to help these defenders of the Christian faith.

Acre was now part of the Turkish Empire. Christians were viewed with suspicion. As a wandering surgeon, however, Theo was free to come and go. In the little drinking houses near the docks, he began to make friends. Soon he made a bargain with a Venetian captain to be taken to Cyprus, an island off the coast belonging to Venice. In Cyprus, finding a boat going to Rhodes was simple. Daring gunrunners and smugglers were bringing supplies and people in continually under the noses of the Turkish fleet. One morning, Theo found himself in a Cyprian fishing smack sailing northeast for the beleaguered island.

It was the end of November. The defenders of Rhodes were in serious difficulties. Grand Master Phillipe de L'Isle Adam, the brave commander, had watched his garrison dwindle to one hundred and eighty knights and only fifteen hundred tired soldiers. The autumn rains had brought fever. Now the chilling cold of winter was here. The men shook with ague, and cursed the fate that had brought them to this island of death.

The soldiers of the Sultan Suleiman suffered the same lot as their enemy. Rhodes was a wall of stone, against which the Turk battered his head in vain. Yet Suleiman had greater manpower; little by little, his soldiers had crept closer to the defenses of the knights.

The fishing boat brought Theo to the rear of the Turkish positions in the dead of night. A thin ray of light from a masked lantern was their only guide. The boat had also carried a cargo of naphtha. This liquid was the basic ingredient of the terrible Greek fire. Naphtha was mixed with gunpowder, poured into little pots, and ignited. The pots were then hurled at the enemy by hand, by catapults, or by cannon. Poured down a stone wall at soldiers mounted on climbing ladders, Greek fire was devastating.

Theo had to wait until the cargo had been brought ashore. A line of waiting men stretched from the boat to a secret tunnel in the rocks. The earthen jugs of naphtha were passed from hand to hand. At last the captain of the boat motioned Theo over the side. A hand thrust the lantern into his face.

"Who's this?"

The captain leaned over the gunwale. "Says he's a doctor and wants to help."

The lantern blinded Theo. He could not see the man who held it. "Very well," said the voice, "he can come with us and talk to the grand master about it." Theo felt the point of a dagger pricking his stomach. "This way, Doctor, and no funny business, please."

Theo moved along the line of men toward the tunnel. He could feel them staring at him.

"He must be a madman," muttered someone, "to come to this accursed island of his own free will."

"Or a saint," said another. They all followed Theo and the man with the lantern into the tunnel leading to the grand master's quarters.

As Theo entered, the commander was standing at the narrow slot of a window, looking out to sea. Phillipe de L'Isle Adam was a tall, white-bearded man with noble bearing, but his eyes looked tired. He wore a brightly polished armor breastplate. On a nearby table were his gauntlets and visored helmet.

Adam turned. "Ah, it's you, Jean. The naphtha?"

"Safely delivered." Jean gestured toward Theo with his dagger. "And this stranger with it."

Adam flicked a humorless smile in Theo's direction. "And

140

what sort of amusement would bring a stranger to Rhodes at this moment?"

"Sire," said Theo earnestly, "my name is Paracelsus. I'm known to many as Doctor Paracelsus. I am a master surgeon, with much experience in military injuries. And I am a good Christian. Finding myself in the vicinity of Rhodes, I thought —"

"To come here and risk your neck for us?"

Theo smiled. "I don't blame you for being suspicious. Perhaps, if I tell you my full name — it's Phillip Theophrastus Bombast von Hohenheim. My grandfather, George von Hohenheim of Bavaria, was a Bombast."

"Von Hohenheim! I know the name. A Teutonic Knight, wasn't he? A brave one, too, I remember. He was stationed with us on the island of Cyprus. You are most welcome, young man."

The grand master held his hand out to Theo. "Come, have you eaten? We haven't much, you know, but you're welcome to it. Jean, put that silly toy away. This man is not a Saracen. Oh, we need surgeons badly. There is so much illness these days. The nights are cold, and our clothing supply has run short. Come, let me show you the hospital —" Beaming with joy, Adam led Theo out of the room.

The sick wards swarmed with sick and dying men. The rooms were lighted by naphtha torches stuck in the walls. The air was dank and fetid; the patients stank with filth. A handful of surgeons and some Greek women who served as nurses struggled desperately to cope with an impossible situation. Theo saw the fires heating pots of boiling oil; he frowned at the horrible messes in the pharmacy. Everyone there, the doctors, the nurses, and the patients, was dirty and tired. All had given up hope.

For a week, Theo worked like a madman. He had sea water brought into the hospital and warmed it in great caldrons. Then he gave orders for the patients to be washed clean from head to foot. He overturned the pots of boiling oil, and used soothing salves for festering wounds. He brewed concoctions of herbs that staved off the chills of fever. Each new attack by the Turks brought more patients, hacked, crushed, and burned. Theo hated war, the cause of his work; but he loved the business of healing, of sewing torn scraps of flesh together to make whole bodies again.

Suddenly, a rumor flew through the camp: the Turkish sultan had offered liberty to all men in the garrison if the knights surrendered. No one's wealth or property would be taken away. Residents would be free to stay on Rhodes if they wished. Suleiman only wanted an end to the useless slaughter.

Now the morale of the garrison began to crack. Where all had seemed hopeless before, there was a chance of life. Soldiers met the attacks of the Turks halfheartedly. The enemy began to move deeper and deeper into the defenses of Rhodes.

Instinctively, Theo knew his task was over. He had no desire to be present when the Turks overran the stronghold of the knights. No one knew how trustworthy the word of a Mohammedan was. Theo did not want to die needlessly on a pile of rocks in the Mediterranean Sea. He made cautious inquiries of men who were beholden to him for their lives.

The night before the formal surrender of the knights to the Emperor Suleiman, Theo slipped out of the same tunnel through which he had come to Rhodes. The few gold pieces he passed to a waiting fisherman paid for his passage to the island of Crete. Theo carried with him his sword Azoth, his instruments, and his notebooks. He did not learn for some years that Suleiman kept his word and spared the lives of all on Rhodes. By then, the epoch of the knights had ended in the Christian world; history had nothing more for them to do.

Over a period of months, Theo wandered from island to island in the Greek archipelago. He visited the island of Kos, where the greatest of all ancient physicians, Hippocrates, had practiced his art. He stopped off at Samos, the birthplace of the ancient mathematician, Pythagoras. He stayed awhile at Lesbos, for here had been born the ancient doctor after whom Theo had been named, Theophrastus of Eresos. He traveled eastward to Constantinople, the metropolis of the Ottoman Empire. In this city of domed mosques and tall minarets, Theo watched Oriental physicians heal their patients without using the monstrous practices of western medicine.

In their pharmaceutical formulas, these doctors used herbs that Theo had never seen. What impressed him most was their concern for the patient's peace of mind; they believed that a proper mental attitude was an important part of the cure. They always regulated a patient's diet carefully, and their surgery was the most skillful he had ever witnessed. A description of the practices and drug recipes of these doctors went into his notebooks.

His path turned back to Venice, and then further north, to the Alps and the Brenner Pass. It was the first week in February, 1524, that Theo stamped the snow from his boots on the steps of his father's house in Villach and knocked on his father's door.

The embrace between Doctor Wilhelm and his son was a joyous one. They stood thus for a long moment, oblivious to the cold winter wind blowing down from the Villacher Alp.

"What am I thinking of?" Doctor Wilhelm released his son's shoulders. "Come in, come in! Here, let me help you with that knapsack. That sword! Have you become a man-at-arms?" Laughing and chattering, they entered the house. Theo looked about the room. It was good to be able to return to a familiar place.

"Twelve years!" exclaimed Doctor Wilhelm. He and Theo were sitting before the fire, sipping glasses of sweet red wine. For a few moments, Theo had the illusion that nothing had changed since he had last sat in this room. But then the fire flared up, and he saw that Doctor Wilhelm's face had many more lines and that his hair had become white. And Theo knew that his father had the same thoughts: my son looks years older; he is becoming a little bald; the furrows in his face have deepened.

"Twelve years!" repeated the doctor. "What has happened to you in all that time? Are you really a doctor of medicine? Have you been practicing your art? What cities have you —"

"Wait, wait, Father!" protested Theo with a laugh. "One question at a time, please. First, how has it been with you?"

Doctor Wilhelm waved his hand to draw in the circle of the room. Theo could see how it was; little had changed. He still taught and worked at the Fugger school of mines. Johann was still the chief alchemist. "Johann should be here soon. We spend many evenings together, as old cronies should."

There was a knock on the door. Theo rose to open it; there stood Johann. For a moment, the little alchemist rubbed his

eyes in disbelief. Then, with a cry, he sprang forward and embraced Theo. "Theo! My little alchemist! To think that I have lived to see you again!"

Theo had not expected such an emotional outburst from the man he remembered as a sharp-tongued taskmaster.

"Johann has always thought of you as his own son," said Doctor Wilhelm with a gentle smile. He went to the sideboard to pour a glass of wine for Johann. The three sat about the fireplace, while Theo recounted his adventures.

Doctor Wilhelm had replenished the fire many times before the saga was done. Now he rose to thrust a fresh log into the embers. "And all this has happened to my son? How you have surpassed me in knowledge and experience!"

"If that is so, I have you to thank, Father. You were the one who inspired me to think about medicine the way I do."

"Now tell me some more," put in Johann, "about those ideas you have for using alchemy in medicine."

Theo smiled. "Nothing more than you yourself taught me about using alchemy in the study of minerals, Johann. If the hidden ingredients of herbs and animals can act as remedies for sickness, why not the hidden ingredients of the minerals?"

"But most of them are poisonous. Instead of healing, you would be killing people!"

"That's what the academic physicians are doing now with their hocus-pocus medicine. Look here, I have experimented with these mineral drugs. Isn't that what you preach in your laboratory, Johann — experimentation? Well, I have just carried your idea over into medicine. And I have found that the answer is in the correct dosage. The art of alchemy has a place in medicine, and I mean to see that it achieves that place."

"Ah," said Johann, "now I begin to understand the real meaning of that name: *Paracelsus*. It fits you well. You have indeed gone far beyond Celsus! But tell me some more of your work."

Theo warmed up to his subject. Here was an audience ready to understand him. "Most important of all, I believe, is for physicians to study alchemy. No doctor should be allowed to graduate and practice without a solid foundation of experimentation in alchemy."

"Hear, hear!" exclaimed Doctor Wilhelm. "A fine theory, my son. But what will the university people say to it?"

"They will try to hang me for it," said Theo cheerfully,

"but they will find that they are trying to stop a flood with a bucket of sand. Alchemy is inseparable from medicine; and medicine will not progress until that fact is realized. Did I tell you about my experience with the French disease? I watched the pure quicksilver treatment kill men, and saw the guaiac wood treatment choke them to death. But when I dissolved the quicksilver in acid and evaporated off the liquid, I had a new form of quicksilver — a red salt. I knew it would be poisonous in ordinary amounts. But in very minute quantities? It worked like a charm. The sores of the French disease disappeared. My patients were reborn."

"The Fugger family wouldn't like to hear you say that about guaiac wood." Johann grinned. "They are making a fortune, importing the stuff from the New World."

"Let's be practical," said Doctor Wilhelm, "and discuss your future. What plans have you made?"

"Why not remain here, in Villach?" put in Johann eagerly. "There is room for a good doctor in town. And we could work together in the laboratory on your new ideas."

"That's a very tempting offer," said Theo. "But I haven't decided yet —" He rubbed his eyes. "And I'm really very tired —"

Doctor Wilhelm leaped to his feet. "And we are two very selfish old men to make you sit here and talk so late. Good night, Johann! Let this poor boy get some sleep."

"I get the hint!" Johann wrung Theo's hand. "Good night, my boy. You have become the kind of man I had hoped you would. And think it over — I mean, about Villach." The door closed behind him.

Up in his room, Theo removed his clothes. His own bed felt

soft and comforting. As he felt delicious sleep coming on, his last thought was: how pleasant it would be to stay here with the ones who want me most!

Several days later, however, when Doctor Wilhelm pressed him for an answer, Theo no longer felt the same. By daylight, Villach seemed a small, stagnating mining village, compared with the great cities he had seen. He could not repress the urge to be off again.

Doctor Wilhelm was sad but resigned. "Where will you go now?"

"I had thought of Salzburg in Germany. I have heard that there is need of a good physician there."

Doctor Wilhelm shrugged. He knew this wanderlust was something he could not fight. He only hoped Theo would return again soon. "Before I leave this world," he added.

Tears rushed to Theo's eyes. He embraced his father and promised to return as soon as he had established himself. Again, the von Hohenheims, father and son, waved farewell to each other.

Much had happened in Germany since Theo had spent his time traveling from university to university. The theology professor at Wittenberg, Martin Luther, had intensified his quarrel with the authorities of the Church at Rome. In 1517, when Theo was with the Spanish soldiers in North Africa, Luther had nailed to the door of the Wittenberg church a paper on which he had written ninety-five different arguments against the ways of the leaders in Rome. Moreover, Luther had proposed a new attitude toward sin and salvation. If a man felt that he would be pardoned for his sins by God, if he had within himself the *faith* that this would happen, then salvation would be his. Such an idea was an outright heresy to the Church leaders, for it meant that an authoritative body like the priesthood would no longer be necessary.

Three years later, in 1520, when Theo was a military surgeon in Sweden, Martin Luther had been excommunicated from the Church by Pope Leo X. In a complete act of rebellion, Luther burned the pope's letter in the public square of Wittenberg. Germany was rent into two factions, those who sided with Luther and those who were for the Church. The followers of Luther were called Protestants. Many princes who had been taxed heavily by the Church willingly became Protestants in order to escape this burden. The peasants of Germany, long oppressed by taxation, seized this opportunity to revolt both against the Church and their lot as serfs.

When Theo came to Salzburg in 1524, he found himself in a hotbed of revolt. The wife of a nobleman had ordered the serfs on her estate to spend their Sundays gathering snail shells so that she could make ornamental pincushions. This meant that her peasants lost the one day of rest they had during the week. They refused to obey her. When she had some of them whipped, the peasants of the surrounding countryside became aroused. The revolt had spread all through the south and east of Germany. Though the peasants had few guns, they had scythes, flails, and pitchforks. They had been oppressed for so many years that many would rather die than remain serfs.

At first, the wealthy landowners and noblemen had been taken completely by surprise. The vengeance of the peasants was a terrible thing. Blood was spilled without reason; women

and babes-in-arms died simply because they happened to live in castles and not in huts.

Now the princes of Germany were beginning to rally against the peasants. Even Luther, frightened by the rebellion his teachings had stirred up, denounced the peasants for their madness. The noblemen decided on a policy of extermination in order to show their power over the serfs. No quarter was given on either side.

On Theo's second night in Salzburg, he walked from his lodgings to a small inn where he had found the food appetizing. He sat at a table, ordered his dinner, and looked about him. In the light of the torches and candles, the dining room had a cavelike appearance. Here and there, men sat in twos or threes at tables. There were no large groups as there had been at the Red Donkey Inn in Tübingen. Conversation was being carried out in low tones, almost whispers.

A plate of steaming soup was set before Theo. As he took a sip, he heard a voice at the next table exclaim loudly, "No, by God, the burgomaster will not get away with it!"

Theo looked up. There was some thing familiar about the voice. The man who had spoken realized that he had shouted. Flushed with embarrassment, he looked about him. His eyes met Theo's. After a whispered conversation with his companion, the man arose and approached Theo's table.

"May I ask your name, sir?"

"Paracelsus — Doctor Paracelsus." Theo half arose, his eyes searching the man's face, trying to remember where he had seen him before.

"No relation to a certain Theo von Hohenheim, by any chance?"

Theo sprang to his feet. "Hans! Hans Ziller! By all that's holy!" And the two fell into each other's arms. They danced about the room, clapping each other on the back, shouting and laughing.

"I thought you'd be a rich, fat medico by this time, stuffed into velvet cloth and being spoon-fed by six liveried servants."

"And I thought you'd be a lean vulture of the law, waxing wealthy on the savings of widows and orphans."

The patrons of the tavern watched this strange scene in wonder.

"Come, finish your meal," said Hans, "and we'll go to my rooms and talk. How many years has it been? Fifteen?"

"Closer to seventeen," muttered Theo through a mouthful of soup.

Hans turned and motioned to the man who had been sitting at the table with him. The other nodded, rose, and slipped quietly out of the tavern.

Theo watched. "What was that all about?"

"I can't talk here." Hans looked mysterious. "Wait until we get to my house."

Hans led Theo through dark twisting side streets. Once he pulled Theo into the protecting shadow of a doorway as a small group of armed men came clumping past. "Municipal guards," hissed Hans. "There's a special curfew for the whole city."

Safe in the lawyer's apartment, Theo exploded. "What the devil, Hans! Have you become a court spy? What sort of intrigue is going on?"

"Man, where have you been?" cried Hans. "Have you learned nothing since you left Tübingen? Luther has defied the pope. The world is in flames."

"I have been too busy tasting of the world's wonders to care about such things," said Theo. He told Hans a little about his wanderings.

"Very interesting," said Hans, "but right here is where men of your ability are needed. Remember, Theo, that I once said I was sick of being a peasant? That I was going to become a rich lawyer?" Theo nodded. "Well, I became a lawyer, all right. And I have done well. But once a peasant, always a peasant. The peasants of Germany are revolting against their masters, Theo. God has given them the sign. And Hans Ziller is in their revolt up to his neck."

Theo looked bewildered and said nothing. Hans continued: "The Archbishop of Salzburg has pledged himself to exterminate the peasant army in this region. His hired soldiers are marching now to where they think that army is. But they won't find it!"

"How do you know?"

"Because I, Hans Ziller, told the archbishop where to march. Instead of the peasant army headquarters, his hired assassins will find a peasant ambush and death."

Theo's eyebrows went up. "Then you are a —"

"Yes, I am the liaison between the peasants and the city of Salzburg. My job is — well, you might say master spy, controller of information — whatever you want to call it. The cynical young college boy you knew is no more, Theo. Now I am fighting for a cause in which I believe with all my heart: freedom for the German serf!"

Theo jumped up and clasped Ziller's hand. "And one in which I believe with all my heart, too, Hans! Perhaps my grandfather was a Teutonic Knight. But I have lived among peasants and miners, and I am one of them, not a nobleman. What can I do to help you?"

From that night on, there began for Theo one of the strangest roles ever played by a doctor of medicine. The headquarters of the peasant army was hidden on one of the heavily forested hills outside of Salzburg. Theo helped establish a general hospital, where men could receive treatment. Since his physician's robe guaranteed him unchallenged passage through the city gates at any hour, he could carry secret messages in and out of the city at any time.

Hans taught him the little tricks of espionage: how to estimate the size of a body of soldiers, and how to get information from barmaids in whom soldiers had confided. Theo learned to be a "devil's advocate." At night, he would come into a tavern where the citizenry gathered. He would begin a good-natured discussion with someone, and then slyly make insinuations about the peasant uprising. This usually led to an uproar. Before he disappeared from the inn, Theo would make sure that the townspeople were won over to the peasants' side.

At the same time, during the day, he practiced medicine innocently in the city. Theo enjoyed the danger and suspense of this double life. At first it was frightening. He found it hard not to cringe, not to jump into the nearest doorway, if any of the archbishop's guardsmen passed by. But his physician's immunity soon gave him the confidence he needed. The whole affair became an exciting game.

One evening, as he prepared to leave his room, there was a loud knock on the door. Theo looked about wildly. Was it the Archbishop's Guard? His window was three stories above the street; he was trapped! Again the knocking sounded, this time with a desperate banging. A man's voice called, "Doctor Paracelsus! Open, I beg you!"

Theo knew the voice. It was Hans Ziller's assistant, the man who had been at the table that first evening. Theo flung open the door. "What's wrong, Conrad?"

Conrad was out of breath. His clothing was in disarray; when he spoke, his voice was a hoarse croak. "Got to — to get out! Archbishop knows — everything! All the men of Salzburg are going to be arrested tonight!"

Theo shook him by the shoulders. "Get hold of yourself! How do you know this? Where's Hans?"

Conrad choked. "Gone — murdered! There was a spy in our midst! Now you must go — quickly!"

Theo looked about him. "My drugs? My clothing?"

"There is no time! Take only what you can carry in your hands. The archbishop's men are at my heels!"

Theo seized the sword Azoth and buckled it about him. He thrust his precious vial of laudanum into a pocket, picked up the rucksack with his notebooks, and, together with Conrad, plunged down the stairway to the street. Avoiding the main streets, they soon came to the western gate of Salzburg. Here, Theo pretended that he was on an emergency call to a nearby nobleman's castle and that Conrad was his helper.

"All right, Doctor," said the guard, "pass. But be mighty careful. Those peasants out there don't care who they murder in the dark."

With this warning ringing in his ears, Theo walked out on the dark public highway, away from Salzburg. Conrad soon left him to meet the peasant leaders, who were moving their headquarters to a different place. Theo decided to go on; he felt that the revolt was a lost cause. Time was to prove him right. The peasants were crushed by the power of the nobility.

Again, for the next year, Theo became a wanderer. For a while, he worked in the alchemist's laboratory at Neuberg Castle, the home of the Duke of Bavaria. The chief alchemist was being paid by the duke to find the philosopher's stone. He and Theo, however, spent most of their time doing experiments with metals, in an effort to produce substances which could be used as remedies for disease. But soon Theo felt that his work here was finished.

His path lay toward the west. In city after city, he prac- ticed his medical art. He knew that the cures he accomplished were the result of experimentation and understanding of na-

155

ture. But to the people, his ability to cure diseases was magical. Everyone spoke with awe and reverence of the young Doctor Paracelsus, who could call upon the spirits dwelling in herbs and metals to cure illnesses. The poor, who could not possibly afford the services of a doctor, eagerly awaited the coming of this strange young man, who wore a great sword strapped to his waist. Doctor Paracelsus always treated any who were ill and charged nothing for his work. He was grateful for a simple meal and a bottle of wine.

Finally, Theo came to the city of Strassburg, an opulent center of business and culture. Some of the finest books in the world were printed on the Strassburg printing press. Theo found Strassburg the only city in Germany where surgeons had equal rights with physicians.

Here, he decided, is where I ought to settle down. What do I achieve by all this wandering? I am always alone — I have no one. In Strassburg, perhaps, I shall make friends — have a normal, happy life . . .

He applied for official citizenship and was accepted. He paid his fee to the doctors' guild, an organization he had to join in order to practice. There was a guild for every profession in each large city of Europe. Without the guild's seal of approval, anyone was simply an outsider, unable to practice his art.

Theo rented a suite of rooms and began to practice medicine. He hoped to become friends with the physicians who taught at the surgeon's college. But he had forgotten that his name was anathema to the academic physicians. His enemies, the defenders of the old medicine of the books, had spread the word throughout Europe: condemn Paracelsus.

156

He received a challenge from the anatomy lecturer, Doctor Hock, at the surgeon's school. Would the great Paracelsus debate with him in public on the subject of anatomy?

Theo brushed the challenge aside. "I have no time for such stupidities," he told the people who called on him. "I am in Strassburg to heal the sick, not to waste time with words. But I shall be glad to give the good Doctor Hock private lessons in the treatment of gunshot wounds and pike thrusts."

The college surgeons spread the rumor that Doctor Paracelsus was afraid to debate with Hock. The reason? Why, the great Doctor Paracelsus was just an ignoramus!

Theo's practice languished. Where forty people had appeared at his door each morning, now only two or three came. Most of the townspeople believed the gossip about him. Theo paced up and down in his empty consulting room. He felt unsure of himself, as he had years ago in the olive groves of Italy. Did Doctor Paracelsus really deserve the title of Doctor?

In the city where Theo had sought peace and security, he had found only distrust and persecution. Sadly, he began to pack his belongings once more.

Chapter Seven

Doctor Paracelsus! Doctor Paracelsus!" A hand rapped on Theo's door.

"My door is open to all," said Theo. He stood facing the doorway, arrested in the act of stuffing some hose into his pack.

The man who entered was dressed for riding. He wore long boots that came up to his knees, a brown leather jerkin, and a broad-brimmed hat. Theo could see the horse's sweat still gleaming on the sides of his boots.

"Thank heaven, I found you, sir! I have come a long way."

Theo thrust the hose into the knapsack. "What do you want of me?"

"My master sends for you. He lies grievously ill, and no doctor can cure him."

"He can't be a citizen of Strassburg, then!" muttered Theo.

"Oh no, sir, not of Strassburg. Of Basel, Switzerland. My

master is the famous printer of books, Master Froben. He has a great sore on his leg which will not heal. He has been bled and purged by the best doctors in Switzerland. Alas, the wound does not close."

"How does he know about me?"

"The name of the great Swiss physician, Doctor Paracelsus, is well known in Basel. Everyone speaks of your miracles —"

"Except the doctors, I'll wager! Well, I won't deny that I've learned more about the practice of medicine than they will ever know." Theo looked down at his well-worn knapsack. There were words written in notebooks packed away there that the doctors of Strassburg would never understand. And here he was, Theophrastus von Hohenheim, Doctor Paracelsus himself, packing, getting ready to run like a whipped cur.

The coming of this servant was a sign, he told himself. To the man he said simply, "I will come."

The city of Basel was the cultural center of Switzerland. Here were gathered many of the great scholars of Europe. The publishing house of Froben was a center of attraction for them. Froben himself cared for the scholars' needs and published their books. He was a man of great wealth and influence.

Theo entered Froben's house with some apprehension. His experience at Strassburg had shaken his confidence in himself. He followed the servant up the staircase. The house was richly furnished, with tapestries on the walls and velvet drapings at the windows. It was filled with people, all of whom stared at Theo with mournful expressions. Theo sensed that they felt it was a house of death.

Froben lay on a large canopied bed in the center of a spacious bedroom. Even though it was noon, the drapes of the canopy were drawn and the windows were shuttered. The room was lighted by many candelabras.

When Theo entered the bedroom, he was met by a woman whose eyes were filled with tears. He realized that she was Frau Froben. She grasped Theo's hand. "You are our last hope, Doctor Paracelsus."

Theo looked about the room. He pointed to the windows. "Why are the shutters closed?"

"The doctors said that the miasmas of the outer air were dangerous."

"They are imbeciles!" Theo turned to the servant. "Put out the candles. Let the sun into the room." The man ran to do his bidding.

When Theo pulled back the drapes of the canopy, he saw that the publisher Froben was indeed ill. There seemed to be almost no flesh in his face; the skin was stretched tautly over sharp bones. Froben smiled when he saw Theo, a weak smile that made the cheekbones stand out more sharply than before.

"So this is the fabulous Doctor Paracelsus! I expected an older man. Well, I hope I haven't brought you to Basel for nothing."

Theo said nothing. He drew the canopy drapes and examined Froben. The ulcer in the publisher's leg was a broad, deep well of pus. Theo could see the angry red of the infection spreading up into the thigh. Froben groaned; he was in great pain. Theo saw that his body was emaciated; many little cuts on the skin testified to the many times Froben had been bled. Theo remembered the university doctors in Paris and the case they had dared him to cure.

A great sigh escaped Froben. "I suppose the leg will have to come off, eh, Doctor?"

"What gave you that idea?" asked Theo.

"That's what the last physician said. I repeat his words: 'I am afraid that the only remedy, my good sir, is immediate amputation.'"

"And what did you say to that?"

"I had him kicked out of my house!"

Theo laughed. "Good for you! That's probably the first sensible treatment he's ever had. Now look here, Master Froben, I believe I can cure your leg. But you must do as I say — complete faith, you understand? I am not one of your book doctors, gabbling about Galen. I am a healer of men, and I understand the ways of nature. Follow my instructions, and you'll walk again on two legs."

Froben smiled again. "By God, I believe you mean it. Very well, Doctor Paracelsus, order away!"

Theo opened the drapes and summoned the servant. "Get some men up here and move this bed next to the window. I want this patient to get some sun on his body. And please fetch my knapsack." The man's eyebrows went up, but he left to do Theo's bidding.

To Froben's wife, Theo said, "Your husband needs good solid food. I'll wager those ignoramuses you called in have been feeding him nothing but gruel." She nodded, open-mouthed. "Well, madam," he continued, "if you want a live, healthy husband, I would suggest that you prepare him a meal of roast fowl, bread, and good red wine at once. And please have some boiling water and clean towels sent up right away."

She stood for a moment in a state of shock and then fled to the kitchen.

Theo gave only two more orders: first, that plenty of clean linen bandages be brought, and second, that a cot be moved into Froben's room. For two weeks, Theo did not leave his patient's side. He cleansed the ulcer daily and applied a stronger salve of metallic salts than he had used in Paris. He examined all the secretions of his patient carefully: the color of the urine, the consistency of the stools, the color of the blood, the ropiness of the saliva. Once a day, Theo laid hot compresses on the area about the ulcer. He fed Froben easily digested food, like chicken and lamb. At night, he gave Froben small amounts of laudanum to insure an easy sleep.

Little by little, the miracle was worked. The purple at the edge of the ulcer disappeared, along with the red streaks under the skin. And as the hole of the ulcer filled in with new healthy tissue, Froben's cheeks began to fill out. Three weeks after Theo had taken up residence in his bedroom, the publisher got up and took his first fumbling steps.

"Well, Master Froben, I think you no longer have need of my services." It was a week later. Theo sat at the supper table with his patient.

Froben shook his head. "I can't believe it! There I was, staring the angel of death right in the face. I had given up, I tell you! All that cupping and bleeding, and those nasty concoctions — and when that fellow came in bleating about cutting the leg off, I knew the game was over. And then you came along — and here I am!"

Theo smiled. "You haven't heard my fee yet."

Froben spread his hands. "Ask what you will. Of what use is money to a dead man?"

"I am not particularly interested in money," said Theo, "although I will admit it comes in handy sometimes. Master Froben, what I want is recognition." Theo arose and poked about in his knapsack. He returned with a sheaf of papers in his fist. "Look, here are some of the papers I have written."

Froben examined the titles. *"Treatise on Dropsy, on the Coughing Sickness, on Gout, on Apoplexy.* Hmmm! What's this one — *On the Diseases That Deprive Man of His Reason?* What do you mean by that title? True, I don't know much about medicine. But isn't madness caused by the demons working within a person?"

Theo shook his head. "I hold this superstitious folly to be one of the greatest errors of European doctors. I have examined many mad people. I have cured some. No one will ever cure them by flinging them into dungeons, or by chaining them to stone walls. Madness is a true medical disease which afflicts man's soul. And it is the physician's duty to treat it as he treats diseases of the body."

Froben had been shuffling through the papers. "Why are you showing these to me?" he asked.

"What I want for my fee, Master Froben," repeated Theo slowly, "is recognition. I want other doctors, medical students, surgeons, and alchemists to hear what I have to say. I want them to read the books I am going to write. Because I, Paracelsus, have learned much about diseases and their treatment that is unknown to most doctors. University medicine is stagnant and stale. The men who teach it have minds that are yellowed and wrinkled like the ancient books they worship. I can breathe new life into their work. I offer them the new medicine — experimental medicine!"

Carried away, Theo was standing and pounding the table with his fist. Froben put a hand out to stop him.

"Hold, hold, my good Paracelsus. You don't have to preach from your pulpit to me. I believe you mean exactly what you say. Now then, what you want, it seems to me, is an opportunity to lecture at the University of Basel." Froben paused a moment, chin on fist, staring into space. "Yes, I believe I can arrange that. And perhaps a bit more. We shall see, Doctor Paracelsus. Give me a few days. Perhaps you will receive your long-awaited recognition." He was about to continue, when he was interrupted by a knock on the door.

The man who entered was elderly, and wore a long, black dressing robe. He had a rather long, sharp nose and a wide mouth. It was his eyes that attracted Theo; they were gentle, yet intelligent and searching.

"Forgive me," he said to Froben in a low, pleasant voice. "I do not mean to intrude, dear friend. But I heard of your recovery, and hoped I might be allowed to come and see you in a restored state."

"You see before you a whole man," declared Froben, "and here is the genius who is responsible. Doctor Paracelsus, this is my good friend, Desiderius Erasmus. I have the good fortune to have him in my house as a guest."

Theo shook the proffered hand heartily. "It is my great pleasure to meet you, sir. Who has not heard of Erasmus of Rotterdam? When I left Ferrara in 1515, they were still chuckling over the anecdotes in your little book, *Adagia*. And as

little as I like Latin, I must confess that I could not put the
book down once I had begun to read it."

Erasmus' face flushed with pleasure. "It is kind of you to
mention it."

"Look here, Erasmus!" Froben thrust Theo's work at him.
"I want you to look at the papers this young man has written.
Some of this has a touch of genius. As much as I can under-
stand of it, of course."

Erasmus took the treatises and promised gravely to read
them through. "And if you can spare a moment, Doctor," he
added in a rather plaintive tone, "I would be grateful if you
would examine me. I haven't been feeling well lately, and I
do not understand why. My apartment is just upstairs." Theo
promised he would come.

While he waited for the promised fruits of Froben's gratitude, Theo lived in the publisher's house. All his needs were
cared for. Even better was the opportunity of meeting many of
the famous writers of Europe. He met John Oecolampadius,

the foremost Protestant pastor in all Switzerland. Froben introduced him to a man named Boniface Amerbach. "Here is the grandson of John Amerbach, the man who taught me to be a printer and publisher; now Boniface is a great writer and I publish his books."

One day, a rather heavy-set man came to the house, wearing a red beret and a loose, colorful cloak. His face was round, with a large nose and full lips. He wore a beard cut square, in the Spanish style.

"Ah, Holbein!" cried Froben with obvious delight. "I want you to meet the man who saved my life. This is Doctor Paracelsus."

Holbein held his arm in the gesture artists use to measure a proportion. "That bold forehead! Those eyes that seem to look into the future! I must put your face on canvas!"

Theo was delighted. "To have my portrait painted by the great Holbein would indeed be an honor."

Six months went by without a word from Froben about his plans for Theo. Meanwhile, there was plenty for Theo to do. Froben's many friends came to him for treatment. He examined Erasmus and found that the famous writer was suffering from a mild arthritis in his joints. He explained that this was a natural disease of old age, and prescribed a drug that would ease the pain.

Erasmus sent him a note: ". . . you have brought my best friend back from the shadows of death, and you have restored me as well. As for your writings, I have read them. I know little about medicine, but I was able to feel the very deep truth of your words. I hope you will remain in Basel for many years . . ."

166

One afternoon, Theo was sitting in his room, reading his notes for a book he planned to write on surgery. There was a knock on the door, and Froben entered.

"Put away your papers, my dear friend, and let us talk." Froben sat in the chair Theo had hastily pulled up. "I have made arrangements which I believe will pay my debt in full. First, the city council has met and, at the urging of myself and Oecolampadius, has elected you municipal physician of Basel. You will be responsible for all measures pertaining to sanitation and the health of the citizens. This means that you will also inspect all the apothecary shops. How does that sound to you?"

"That is a great honor," said Theo, "but —"

"Hear me out," interrupted Froben, "there is more. The municipal physician is automatically appointed professor of medicine at the University of Basel. You will have the privilege of wearing the cap, gown, and hood. And what is more, you may lecture at the university, if you wish."

Theo rose and clasped Froben's hand. "Master Froben, this is far more than I had wished for! Now I can have students! Now others will hear my ideas!" Suddenly, his face fell. "I'll wager that the university people aren't very happy about it."

Froben dismissed his anxiety with a wave of the hand. "Don't worry about them. They won't dare bother you. You will be free to do as you wish." He rose to go, but first he turned and offered Theo his hand. "My congratulations, Professor Paracelsus."

As the door closed behind Froben, Theo sank into his chair. Plans began to buzz around in his head: there was so much he wanted to do! But first, he remembered to write a letter to

167

Villach, telling Doctor Wilhelm and Johann the good news.

Conscientiously, Theo began his inspection of the apothecary shops of Basel. To his dismay, he found most shops filthy beyond belief. In many of them, medicines were mixed carelessly, often by apprentices who had not yet learned their job. Many of the pharmacists had secret agreements with the town physicians; for each patient directed to his shop the apothecary remitted part of his fee to the physician.

Theo instituted an organized cleanup of the apothecary shops. Even to begin this, he had to fight the pharmacists' guild tooth and nail. The city magistrates, however, were on Theo's side, and directed the apothecaries to obey his instructions. Among the pharmacists of Basel, the name of Doctor Paracelsus was spoken to the accompaniment of a curse and a spitting on the floor.

Meanwhile Theo, aware only of the good he was going to accomplish, made plans for a series of lectures at the University of Basel. His tasks as city physician occupied much of his time; he was unable to prepare his lectures in time for the winter term. Nevertheless, Theo managed to spend some hours, often long after midnight, outlining his subject matter.

One day, a young man came and begged to become Theo's disciple. "My name is Johann Herbst," he said. "I have heard of your miracles and I wish to serve you as my master." Theo was impressed by this adulation; when he found that Johann could read and write Latin fluently, he hired him as his secretary. "One favor," begged Johann, "call me by my Latin name — Oporinus." With a smile, Theo agreed; he remembered the pride he had first taken in being known as *Para*celsus. Oporinus wrote official letters for Theo and, in general, directed the routine of the office of municipal physician.

It was not until the summer of 1527 that Theo was ready to give his first lecture. As was the custom, he posted an announcement at the university:

"Thanks to the kindness of the authorities at Basel, I, Theophrastus Paracelsus Bombast von Hohenheim, Doctor of Medicine, will lecture daily at the University on the following subjects: General Pharmacy and the writing of prescriptions; Special Pathology of the Human Body and Treatments; Internal Diseases, stomach-ache, consumption, gout, toothache, asthma, etc., and their treatment; External Injuries, wounds, skin diseases, cancers, and ulcers; Special Lectures on diagnosis using the pulse and urine; how to use purges and bloodletting properly.

"I, Paracelsus, will teach from my own writings, and not from the rules of the ancients. The barbarous practices of doctors have made medicine a practice of errors rather than an art. I shall attempt to cleanse medicine of these errors and bring the art back to its original pure state. What I have learned, I have learned from experience. A doctor is not great because he is a smooth talker, or knows many languages, or has read many books. What is important is that he understand nature and its deepest secrets. The physician must know the various kinds of diseases, how to diagnose them, and how to cure them by prescribing proper remedies — this knowledge is his business.

"Let all who are willing to be led into these new paths come to Basel to listen to Doctor Paracelsus."

169

The evening of Theo's first lecture, the lecture hall of the university was crowded. Dressed in their robes and colored hoods, curious members of the faculty had come to look at this strange phenomenon, whose name had been linked with magic and mystery. The rest of the audience was made up of medical students, eager to hear the promised words of revolt against authority. Voices buzzed in anticipation of the unknown. Suddenly, the chattering ceased; the lecture hall was silent. Doctor Paracelsus had appeared on the platform.

Theo was resplendent in the full robes of a university physician. For a full moment he said nothing, but fixed his audience with eyes that glowed with realized hopes.

"My colleagues and students," he began, "I stand before you in the costume that is befitting for a medical professor to wear."

"My God," whispered a student in the front row, "he's speaking in German!"

The professors looked at one another. Was the man mad? Or was he merely trying to insult their intelligence? Didn't he know that Latin was the tongue of the learned?

Undismayed, Theo went on. "These fancy garments, however, are not fitting for the true physician!" With a single motion, he cast off his robes and cap and flung them to the floor. Beneath the professional garb, he wore his old laboratory apron, stained by years of use.

"The alchemist's apron!" he shouted. "This is the robe of the true physician who wishes to learn the secrets of nature and to use them to conquer disease!"

Instantly, the lecture hall was in an uproar. Students cheered, whistled, clapped, and stamped their feet. Some professors rose

170

in their seats and howled with indignation, shaking their fists
at the platform. Others bent double, shrieking with laughter.
Theo stood there, staring at them all with defiance. After a few
moments, most of the professors and students, as though a
signal had been given, turned and walked out of the room.

Theo waited until they had left. Then he raised his hand for
silence.

"I assume," he said, "that those of you who are staying are
brave enough to face new ideas without cringing. I shall speak
tonight of a new use for alchemy — as a science which can
be used to discover new remedies for disease. The alchemy you
know — the rapacious search for a way to make gold — is
useless. I have given the new science a name: not alchemy, but
chemistry. It is an experimental science. Its laws do not depend
upon the writings of the ancients.

"I seek no miracles — only an understanding of nature's secrets. You know there are many herbs and plants whose inner juices are beneficial to man's health. I believe that the principal ingredients of those juices can be made in the chemistry laboratory by the correct combination and manipulation of metals and earths and acids. Every physician ought to study chemistry. Every physician must become an experimenter. When every doctor is also a chemist, medicine shall regain its former glory."

Theo paused to note the effect of his words upon the audience. They sat rapt, motionless, bewildered and yet enchanted by these new concepts.

"You know well," Theo continued, "what the ancients stated to be the causes of diseases." He enumerated them upon his fingers: as a punishment of God, as the influence of the Devil, as the influence of the stars, as a disturbance of the humors of the body, as something missing in the body which medicine could restore.

"Now, I recognize a truth in one of these — that the stars have some influence upon our destinies, and so control our states of health. The spirit of Man in the microcosm and the spirit of God in the macrocosm are thus inseparable. But the other causes, as stated by the ancients, are nonsense."

Theo went on to explain the new notions he had conceived about the origins of disease. Man's body is born pure, without poison. However, from the moment feeding begins, poison is brought into the body as part of man's food. Somewhere inside the body, probably in the stomach, the food has to be separated from the poison. If this is not done properly, the body becomes ill.

172

"Each animal is its own alchemist," he reasoned. "Like the chemist in the laboratory, the body sorts out poison from non-poison, and eliminates the cause of disease. When the chemist in the stomach fails to function, the physician must fight the poisons in the body. Poison must be fought with poison. By a knowledge of chemistry, and by experimenting to find proper dosage for chemical remedies, the physician will learn to heal all the diseases of man."

When Theo finished his lecture, there was no applause. Only from Oporinus, seated in the rear, came a loud "Bravo!" But when heads turned to look at him, he fell silent. The members of the audience scratched their heads and appeared mystified. Doctor Paracelsus seemed to have some wonderfully new ideas, but no one was quite sure what they meant.

"Your lecture was magnificent, Master!" Oporinus was speaking, as he and Theo drove back to Froben's house in a carriage.

"Thank you, Oporinus. You are kind to say it. But I'm not so sure that my audience thought so." Theo's head dropped. He felt he had been a failure.

"A prophet is without honor in his own land," quoted Oporinus. "Someday, those fools will know you had the vision to see the future."

Theo looked up. Yes, he said to himself, the medicine of Paracelsus *is* the future. He remembered Doctor Leoniceno and his words: ". . . you may become the best doctor in the whole world!"

"I won't let them crush me!" he cried to his secretary. "The lectures shall continue! I don't care if only one person comes! Doctor Paracelsus will be heard!" And Theo set his jaw in angry defiance of his enemies, as the carriage rolled through the dark, empty streets of Basel.

Through the summer and into autumn, the lectures of Doctor Paracelsus continued. When the attendance was low, Theo publicly invited outsiders to come to the university to hear him. He welcomed alchemists, barber-surgeons, and pharmacists to his lecture hall.

For the university doctors, this was adding insult to injury. The intrigue against Theo increased in intensity. Opposition to his lecturing at the university became more outspoken. Finally, on some pretext, the university officials told Theo that he could no longer use the university lecture hall.

"The Devil take you all!" he said, and straightway rented a large hall in the center of town. Here he continued to lecture on medicine to anyone who cared to listen. His followers among the alchemists and surgeons grew in number. Meanwhile, the number of his detractors among the physicians and pharmacists also increased.

Saint John's Day came, a student holiday given over to merry pranks and jollity. Wine was consumed in large quantities by the students and townspeople. Musicians played in the streets and people danced. Large bonfires were lit in the city squares.

After a good meal at Froben's, Theo and Oporinus ventured out to partake of the festivities. Before the university gates, they encountered a crowd of students, singing and dancing about a huge bonfire. Some students were busily piling more wood on the fire. One of them, near Theo, cried happily, "Thank the Lord, I've finished my course in rhetoric! I give my

174

textbook as a burnt offering!" And he threw a small book into the fire.

Suddenly, Theo thought of a way to make everyone understand what he was trying to change in the study of medicine. It would be a dreadful act of defiance, but people would know what he meant. He seized Oporinus by the arm. "Come with me, quickly!"

He dragged his protesting secretary to the medical school library. The room was empty; on a holiday, no one came to study. There, on a table, lay the great, parchment-bound volume of the writings of Avicenna. This was one of the books to which all medical students were referred by their professors, just as theology professors referred their students to the Bible.

Theo seized one end of the book. "Here, help me with this," he directed the astonished Oporinus.

"What — what —" stammered the secretary; but Theo gave him no answer. Between them, they lifted the heavy book and carried it out into the street.

"Make way! Make way!" shouted Theo, as they approached the mob of students before the gates. As soon as the students saw Theo, they fell silent. One of them, a medical student, pointed his finger in awe. "That's Avicenna! They are carrying Avicenna!"

Standing as close to the bonfire as he could get, Theo, with the help of Oporinus, lifted the volume high.

"Avicenna!" he cried. "Your usefulness upon the earth is finished! I, Theophrastus Paracelsus Bombast von Hohenheim, have superseded you! Let all the misery you have caused go up in smoke!"

And with a great heave, he cast the works of Avicenna into the flames. A long, drawn-out sigh escaped from the mouths of the students. They had watched a heresy being performed! But it was Saint John's Day, a day for doing crazy things. A few moments later, the students were laughing and singing again.

Theo's act infuriated the university professors. His presence in Basel became unbearable to them. In spite of Froben's influence, Theo's enemies plotted in secret. They began whispering campaigns against him: it was said he was a drunkard, a madman, a charlatan, that he was using Froben and the citizens of Basel for his own foul purposes. One day, Oporinus came running into Theo's chamber waving a piece of paper.

"See, Master, see! A terrible thing! This leaflet has been distributed all over the city!"

Theo looked at the paper. On it was printed a caricature

of his portrait. It was horrible: his forehead had been made to bulge out, the eyes were popping, the head was bald. Under the cartoon were the words: The Shadow of Galen Speaking Against Doctor Theophrastus, Whose Name is Rightly Cacophrastus! This title was followed by a Latin poem making fun of Theo's ideas and recommending that he save the medical world by hanging himself.

Theo was almost ill with fury. He demanded that the city council investigate and search out the perpetrator of this insult. He insisted that the city magistrates arrest and punish the guilty parties. But the men in the municipal government had no desire to be mixed up in the affairs of the university. They put Theo off with excuses, and did nothing.

Theo continued his lectures, but his tone was more bitter, and his analysis of the learning of university physicians more acid. He called them thieves and murderers: thieves because they stole a patient's purse for a promised cure, and murderers because they then proceeded to kill the patient. The university doctors retaliated by dubbing Theo the "Martin Luther of medicine."

The situation was intolerable for the professional physicians of Basel. They knew that one way or another, they would have to get rid of Theo. Their chance came in February of 1528.

Froben had been feeling well. But he was not a young man, and the illness of the previous year had sapped much of his strength. Theo had forbidden him to overexert himself.

But Froben loved life and excitement. Ignoring Theo's order, he went to one of the nearby fairs to enjoy the festive atmosphere. There, he suffered a stroke and died.

Now, Theo had lost the one person important enough to

protect him. The medical faculty and the pharmacists wasted no time setting a trap. Their plan was absurdly simple, and Theo walked into it like an unsuspecting kitten.

He received a summons from Canon von Lichtenfels, one of the wealthy landowners in Basel. The canon's servant told Theo that his wealthy master was suffering from a disease no doctor had been able to cure. A hundred gold pieces would be the reward, if Theo could cure him.

Theo went, examined the canon, and decided that the man was suffering from a disease of the spirit that made him think he was physically sick. He gave the canon some pills made of laudanum. Three days later, the canon announced that he was cured, and sent Theo six gold pieces as payment.

Theo sued von Lichtenfels for the other ninety-four gold pieces. But the court threw the case out, insisting that the canon was within his rights. Then Theo proceeded to do just what the university doctors hoped he would do. Outraged, he abused the court, the magistrates, the city council, even the friends he had made at Froben's house. He felt that everyone was against him. He wrote and had printed a lampoon of the city fathers of Basel, writing under it a biting satire on their corrupt ways. He gave some street beggars a few coins to distribute these leaflets from door to door.

A week later, there was a knock at his door. It was Oporinus. "Master, Master, I bring bad news! Boniface Amerbach is downstairs. He says that the magistrates have issued a warrant for your arrest. You must flee from Basel at once!"

Theo was alarmed. "My possessions? My remedies? My books?"

"Leave your things with me. I will look after everything

and bring all to you when you find a place to stay. There is no time, Master! The police are coming tonight!"

Theo buckled on his sword Azoth and threw his cape over his shoulders. At the foot of the stairs, Amerbach waited impatiently.

"Hurry!" he cried. "I have a horse for you at the back door. Ride north to Colmar. My brother is there and will give you shelter."

Theo shook his head sadly. "It seems as though all my adventures must end like this — fleeing in the night from some adversary. Paracelsus against the world! I am alone again!"

Amerbach pushed him to the door. "This is no time for philosophy. Off with you to Colmar! And remember, you are not alone. There are people in Germany who believe in you. Now, go!"

Galloping away through the deserted streets, Theo looked back at the house of Froben. It seemed to him that he had spent the happiest hours of his life there. For once, he had been recognized for what he was and what he knew.

What lay ahead?

Theo knew that his enemies in Basel would not waste time. They would spread their hatred of him through the land, throughout the world.

With friends or friendless, he said to himself, I will keep working. I shall be above them all: Galen, Avicenna, the stupid ignoramuses in the universities. All shall follow me, Paracelsus!

He turned in the saddle and shook his fist at the walls of Basel. "So, you laugh at Cacophrastus, do you? You shall all eat his dirt someday! The doctors of Germany shall look to me as a leader!"

His shout fell away in the darkness. The only answer was the clatter of his horse's hoofs.

Chapter Eight

B Y THE TIME Theo reached the city of Colmar, the news
of his troubles in Basel had already arrived. Basilius
Amerbach spoke readily in Theo's behalf to the Colmar city council. The leaders, however, were afraid of the
mysterious Doctor Paracelsus. They sent a delegation to Theo's
room at the inn where Amerbach had lodged him.

Theo welcomed them in with a flourish. The spokesman of
the delegation, a pompous little man dressed in his best Sun-
day velvet, doffed his hat.

"Doctor Paracelsus, the city of Colmar bids you welcome.
However, there are certain conditions which . . ." His voice
trailed off; he had forgotten the rest of his speech. He looked
beseechingly at the other members.

". . . you must fulfill," whispered one of them.

"Er — yes — you must fulfill." His memory returned suddenly, and he reeled the rest of his speech off rapidly. "You

may not practice medicine, you may not become a permanent resident, you may not publish your books here. You may stay as a temporary resident and guest of Master Amerbach."

Theo took a step forward, and the little man shrank back. "Doctor Paracelsus thanks the good citizens of Colmar," he said in a mocking tone, "for their hospitality. Have no fear; I will not abuse it. And now, if you will excuse me, I have work to do." He bowed them out the door.

Theo seated himself in a chair and gazed out the window. He knew now that his enemies in the universities would never let him rest for a moment. They would spread lies about him, they would make people fear his name all over the world.

But there is one way to fight ignorance, he said to himself. I can write books! Those who can read the printed word will understand what I have to say. I can fight my enemies on paper.

For the next month, he worked like a fury. He spent every moment at his writing desk. From his notes, he wrote a beginning treatise on the French disease. He also began a book on the surgery of wounds. Into this book, he poured all of his experience as a military surgeon.

A month later, Oporinus came, bringing Theo's possessions. With him came some people who had been favorably impressed by Theo's lectures at Basel. They were not academic physicians, but pharmacists, alchemists, and surgeons. Theo welcomed their friendship.

Oporinus and Theo met with this circle of friends every afternoon. It was almost like a king holding court. But in this court, medicine and philosophy took the place of politics and intrigue. Theo's new disciples listened eagerly whenever he

182

spoke. After each meeting, Theo would have a bite to eat and a glass of wine. Then Oporinus would bring his notebooks. Theo would take a pen and write for hours. The words flowed from him like raindrops from a thundercloud. The sword Azoth was only for show; the pen had become Theo's real weapon.

At the end of the year, however, the delegation from the Colmar city council came again. They were sorry, but Doctor Paracelsus had overstayed his welcome. He would have to seek quarters elsewhere. Again, Theo packed his knapsacks.

After a short stay in the city of Esslingen, he came to the city of Nuremberg, stronghold of the Lutherans. Oporinus and a few of his disciples came with him. The citizens welcomed him as a kind of curiosity. The story of his burning of the book of Avicenna had become almost a legend.

Here, Theo had an opportunity to finish his book on the treatment of the French disease. This illness was particularly rampant in Nuremberg when Theo arrived. Sufferers from the French disease were quarantined in a leprosarium outside the gates of the city.

Not long after Theo's arrival, a delegation of academic physicians came to see him. Theo received them with suspicion.

"Doctor Paracelsus," said the spokesman for the group, "we hear that you stand alone against the medical guild in your ideas about the treatment of the French disease. We would like to propose a public debate between yourself and the doctors of Nuremberg on this subject."

Theo smiled disdainfully. He turned to Oporinus, who stood beside him, and said, "A debate! How typically academic!" To the doctor, he said, "I do not waste time debating about disease. I cure disease. Let us practice medicine, instead

183

of talking about it. I offer to treat the French disease and cure it. Can you match that?"

The delegation was thrown into consternation. Why, everyone knew that the French disease was incurable! They buzzed and whispered among themselves. Finally, they agreed that it was a good way to let this Doctor Paracelsus show his own incompetence.

The spokesman stepped forward. "We know how little can be done in the matter of healing the French sickness. But we are content to allow you to try your hand at healing the disease. There is a small hospital outside the Northern Gate where fifteen patients are confined. You may demonstrate your skill on them."

"Thank you, gentlemen," said Theo calmly. "All I will require is the use of an alchemist's laboratory for a week or so. Can you arrange this for me?" The doctors agreed.

Theo found the fifteen victims of this dread disease in a sorry state. Some had been treated with mercury; others with guaiac wood. Nothing had worked. Of the fifteen, four were already in the late stages of the disease; they had great ulcers on their bodies; flesh and bone had been eaten away. Theo knew that he could do nothing for them. In three patients, he detected signs of mercurial poisoning. He stopped their treatment at once. He threw the guaiac wood onto the trash pile.

In the laboratory, Theo diligently prepared compounds from the interaction of mercury with other substances. He boiled, roasted, distilled, and sublimed from early dawn until darkness. The laboratory furnace burned steadily for a week. Theo's face was black with sweat and grime; his apron became freshly stained. Finally, he had the compound he sought. He mixed the chemical carefully into salves and rolled some of it into pills. Then he returned to the leprosarium and began to treat his patients.

Six months later, the same delegation of doctors waited in the anteroom of the leprosarium. Theo entered through a side door and greeted them. "Welcome, my good colleagues. You are ready, I suppose, to examine my patients? First, let me tell you what has happened. Four patients were too far gone to treat; of these, three have already died. Two have not responded to my treatment; however, the disease shows no signs of advance. I am glad to report that nine of the fifteen have been cured."

He made a sign to Oporinus, who stood in the doorway. Nine men walked single file into the room. Theo asked them to remove their shirts. The doctors examined them. Where before there had been the blotches and ulcers of the French disease, there was only clear, healthy skin. The medical delegation stood there, mouths agape. They had witnessed a miracle. At a sign from the leader, they turned to leave the hospital. The last man to leave, however, suddenly turned and ran back. He seized Theo's hand and shook it warmly.

"My congratulations, Paracelsus," he whispered. "I've never seen anything like it! Whatever the others say, I'm for you. You are the greatest doctor in the world!"

Theo's success did not win over the doctors of Nuremberg. Instead, their jealousy grew, and they talked against him. Theo paid little attention to them. "They are frauds," he told Oporinus, "who live off the people like leeches. The victims of their incompetence never live to testify against them!"

Among the people of Nuremberg, Theo's fame increased. Patients from all walks of life came to see him. He made enough money to rent a small house and build a chemistry laboratory. Here, with the help of Oporinus, he attacked the problem of changing mineral salts into forms that could be used as pharmaceutical remedies.

Theo noticed that Oporinus seemed depressed. One day, in the laboratory, he asked his assistant if anything was the matter.

"Ah, Master," sighed the young man, "I am afraid that you do not trust me completely."

"I don't understand what you mean."

"You have not yet told me any of the real secrets of alchemy; the truth as it is revealed to the initiates. You have not yet shown me how to make the philosopher's stone!"

Theo stared at him. "What do you want with the stone?"

Oporinus shrugged. "What does anyone want? To have gold! To be rich!"

Theo threw back his head and roared with laughter. "You fool! How long have you known me? Is this what you think of my alchemy?" He shook his fist under Oporinus' nose. "This kind of thinking has made alchemy a fool's art, not a science. I am interested in discovering the secrets of nature for their own sake, not for gold."

Oporinus looked angry. "Then you will not tell me?"

"There is nothing to tell!" shouted Theo. "Don't be such an idiot!"

"I am an idiot for believing in you!" screamed Oporinus.

Their argument ended in a furious quarrel. The next morning, when Theo awoke, he found that Oporinus had gone.

Theo dismissed the loss with the customary shrug of his shoulders, and hired a small boy to keep the laboratory furnace burning. The atmosphere of smoke and flame, and the violent reactions that occurred during the experiments, frightened the wits out of the boy. He was too proud to admit his fear; but when he came home at night, he told weird tales of hobgoblins and magic potions. Soon, half of Nuremberg believed Theo to be in league with the Devil.

Meanwhile, Theo had not neglected his writing. He finished the first part of his book on the French disease, and persuaded a Nuremberg publisher to print it. While the type was being set, Theo wrote a little pamphlet attacking the guaiac wood treatment as useless. He had this published also; the pamphlet appeared earlier than the book.

The reaction to the pamphlet was far more violent than Theo had expected.

The wealthy Fugger family had invested a good part of its fortune in the importing of guaiac wood from the New World. The use of this wood had become almost a fad with the medical profession. Guaiac was used to treat ulcers and many other skin diseases. The Fuggers were good businessmen. All over Europe, important doctors, whose word on treatment was law, were given shares in the guaiac-importing business.

When the book on the French disease appeared, the Fuggers were aroused. Theo had discredited both the guaiac treatment and the metallic mercury treatment. However, he stated that the mercury treatment could be effective if the metal was changed, by chemistry, into the proper form of its salt.

The Fuggers could not afford to let this lone Doctor Paracelsus ruin their chance for profit. Suddenly, the city fathers of Nuremberg issued a ban against Theo's pamphlet and against the book. The printer refused to print the second part of the book on the French disease. No other printer in Nuremberg would even talk to Theo.

Finally, through secret emissaries, he found a printer who was brave enough to publish his book. Early in 1530 the book, entitled *Three Chapters on the French Disease,* appeared. The uproar in Nurenberg was enough to uproot Theo from his laboratory and house and send him into hiding.

This time, he turned his face southward. He remained for a few months in Beratzhausen, rarely showing his face in public. He stayed in his room and wrote like a fury. Writing became an obsession with him — it was as though he had to sweep all his knowledge out of his head onto paper. Often, he found himself working on several books at the same time.

He concentrated on a pamphlet in which he violently attacked the medical guild, the followers of Galen and Avicenna. He called this pamphlet *Paragranum,* which meant *Against the Grain.* In it, he outlined his concept of the four pillars of medicine: natural science, astronomy, chemistry, and professional ethics. He proclaimed experience and experiment to be the two necessary ingredients of medical progress.

Theo wrote: "Disease and medicine both originate in nature, not in the doctor. What teacher is better for the physician than nature? The art of healing begins with nature, not with the doctor. The physician, then, must begin from nature with an open mind."

He wrote ironically of the doctors who knew so little about remedies that they had to take the advice of pharmacists. "They called me *Cacophrastus* at Basel," he wrote, "but what good does it do them to believe in a *Cacoaristotle* or a *Cacogalen?* The *new* doctors will be chemists. They shall know the

188

mysteries of nature. Where will all the academic quacks go when the new doctors arrive?"

Theo could not find anyone who would print his book. In disgust, he packed again and moved south to the city of Regensburg. Here he finished a book on care for the sick, which he called *The Hospital Book*. "The basis upon which medicine rests is Love," he wrote. He included many of the things he had learned in the east about the hygienic care and diet of sick persons.

One afternoon, he had a visitor from Switzerland. "You do not know me, Doctor Paracelsus," said the man. "I come from St. Gall. Our mayor, Christian Studer, is very ill. We fear for his life. The man we chose to act as mayor suggested that we ask you to come. His name is Vadianus."

At the name, Theo leaped from his chair. "My dear old friend!" he cried. "Vadianus is a man to whom I owe much! Of course, I will come! For him, I would travel to the Antipodes!"

Vadianus had grown older. His hair was white, and he walked with a decided stoop to the shoulders. The sight of his old friend made Theo realize that he himself had now reached the age of thirty-seven.

"Ah, yes," said Vadianus, after greeting Theo, "the university life became too hectic for me. So I retired to this calm and lovely town. And suddenly, I find myself acting mayor. But you, Theo, you seem to have made a name for yourself. Whenever medicine is mentioned, I hear someone say 'Doctor Paracelsus.' "

Theo laughed. "Oh yes, they may speak my name. But not too often in tones of love. Where is your patient?"

Vadianus took him to the mayor's house. A brief examination told Theo that Studer had suffered a stroke. Too much damage had been done; no medicine would be able to restore him. Theo took Vadianus aside and gave him to understand that the situation was hopeless.

"I am sorry that I brought you so far for nothing. At least, let the town pay your fee."

"For you, sir," said Theo, "there will never be a fee."

Vadianus thanked him. "Will you go back to Regensburg?" he asked.

Theo shrugged. "I have nothing to keep me there."

The old teacher put a hand on Theo's shoulder. "Why don't you stay here, in my house?" he asked. "Let me pay your fee in this way. My brother-in-law has a knowledge of alchemical arts; perhaps you and he will have much in common. Please say yes; it would make an old man very happy to have you as his guest."

For Theo, this invitation was the beginning of a pleasant stay of two years in St. Gall. Vadianus saw to it that his physical needs were met. The brother-in-law, Bartholomew Schobinger, knew much of the lore of alchemy. Moreover, he had his own laboratory, and gave Theo permission to use it as his own.

Theo worked happily in the laboratory some of the time, and saw an occasional patient. But most of the time he wrote. An inspiration for a new book had come to him. He would attempt to pierce the surface of nature, to discover the causes of events, and in this way, to explain all of nature.

Alchemical theory, which based all its ideas on two basic substances, Sulfur and Mercury, was to Theo incomplete. He believed there were actually three philosophic substances out of which all matter was composed. Sulfur, yes: this was the fiery or burning principle of matter, the gaseous or burning parts, Mercury, yes: this was the fluid part of matter; the third part was Salt, the solid part of matter. The balance between these three substances in the matter of man's body determined his state of health. If too much Salt built up in the body, then the body became corroded. This is why undigested material in the stomach caused pain. But the Salt could be balanced by adding fluid, the Mercurial part of matter, to wash the Salt away.

God has never permitted a disease to exist, Theo declared, for which He did not also provide a cure.

"Man is his own doctor," he wrote. "The body fights diseases itself by virtue of a force within it which I call the *Archeus*. In fighting disease, the doctor must seek to make the Archeus revitalize the body. Three important rules to follow for keeping disease away are: fresh air, good food, and exercise."

He wrote a chapter on childbirth. This was a subject never discussed by doctors. Attending a birth was undignified for a doctor of medicine; such lowly work was left for the midwife. In his travels, Theo had helped many a peasant wife bring a child into the world. To cut such an important natural event out of the area of medicine seemed to him a ridiculous act. He felt it was a doctor's duty to prevent the various diseases which killed women in childbirth.

Another part of the book was devoted to what Theo called "Invisible Diseases." Here, he wrote about illnesses of the mind. He elaborated upon the ideas of the earlier treatise he had shown Froben. Mentally deranged people were thought to be possessed by the Devil. They were beaten and tortured and often cast into dark dungeons for life. Theo insisted that it was the doctor's place to treat such people. Medicine and love could cure them.

Most of the ideas in this book were unknown in the world of medicine. Theo wanted them printed for every man to read. He often worked without sleep. When exhausted, he would throw himself, fully clothed, upon his bed. After a few hours of sleep, he would rise and continue writing.

When he had finished this daring book, Theo sought for a title. Perhaps I should call it *The Book of Miracles,* he thought. He shook his head. No, he was not a miracle peddler. His ideas were above miracles — beyond them. Ah, that was it! Like Paracelsus — beyond Celsus — he would call this book *Paramirum* — beyond miracles!

He dedicated the book to Vadianus. "You are a man of ideas," he wrote, "who supports medicine. I want to stir your interest in nature, so that you may discover many new truths."

In 1532, the Protestants in Switzerland began to lose ground. John Oecolampadius died in Basel. Another great Swiss Protestant leader, Ulrich Zwingli, was killed in battle. The strife between the Protestant and Roman Catholic parties in Switzerland intensified. Theo decided to leave St. Gall.

He gave his manuscripts to Vadianus. "Keep them for me. I will return for them someday."

Knapsack filled, Theo walked the open road again.

Now, there was a difference. He began to be troubled again by uncertainty. Each night, as he sat by the little fire he had built, he would ask himself: What are you, Paracelsus? Who

are you? What do you believe? In the early hours of the morning, he would wake with a start from a sleep filled with tortured dreams.

Theo began an aimless wandering through Germany. Something inside him had changed. He had lost his arrogance and boastfulness. The material side of existence suddenly lost its meaning for him. Food, clothing, appearance meant nothing. He began to worry about the dilemma of man in the great universe.

He saw three important Beings — like great islands in a sea of emptiness: God, Nature, and Man. I have cared too much about Man, he thought, and I have lost sight of God. I must find my way back across the chasm that separates Man from God.

Theo became a ragged beggar. He spent much of his time in meditation. Once in a while, he preached to anyone who would listen. He ate scraps; more often, he fasted. In many towns, the people would not believe he was a physician. Who had ever seen a doctor in rags? They would rudely show him to the town gates. Be off, beggar, or we'll sic the dogs on you! Doctor Paracelsus, my foot!

Despite his troubled state of mind, Theo managed to keep on writing. But his words now took on a mystical quality. He worried about life and death, and how these were related to God.

"What raises us above our mortal nature," he wrote, "is faith. Through faith, we become like God."

And later: "How can a man say he is certain, when he is so far from any certainty? The truth is that man knows nothing. He does not know the hour of his death, nor does he know any hour of his life or health. God has created him without foreknowledge. As long as the world exists, all will be uncertain.

"No man knows for whom the sun is shining. No man is privileged to take for himself what only God can give him. Everything lies in the hand of God; He gives to whom He desires to give.

"Look how Nature fights against Death! She strives to drive out harsh, bitter Death, whom our eyes cannot see, nor our hands touch. But Nature sees and touches Death and knows him. Therefore, she summons all her power to fight the Terrible One."

Theo thrust the written pages, one by one, into his knapsack. He planned to add them to his previous work, the

Paramirum. The doctor had become a philosopher and a mystic.

Almost two years after he had begun his latest wanderings, Theo found himself in Switzerland again, just beyond the Brenner Pass. The little village of Sterzing lay on his route. He planned to stop there for food and shelter.

As he came down the hillside that overlooked Sterzing, he could see a pall of smoke over the houses. Theo recalled another time when he had seen a similar veil over the roofs of a great city. He knew what it meant. The Black Death had come to Sterzing!

Theo walked slowly down the main street of Sterzing, past the houses nailed shut, past the smoldering fires. A cart filled with bodies of the dead rolled by him on its way to the burying pits. Farther on, he met a small procession led by a priest. Two men carried a long banner on which, in the shape of a cross, were inscribed the letters:

C S
C
S
S R S N S M V
S M Q L I V B
L
N
D
S
M
D
P B

As they marched, the men chanted a hymn in a low mono-tone.

Theo had seen such processions before. The letters on the banner were the first letters of the words of a prayer for aid against the plague. It was believed that, put together, these letters formed a magic word which would drive the plague away from a region. Such superstitious nonsense filled Theo with disgust.

Most of the men walked with their eyes fixed on the ground. A few, however, eyed Theo with suspicion. What kind of fool walked knowingly into a plague-filled town? Even scavengers knew enough to avoid the plague! Theo stopped the last man in the procession and asked if there was a hospital in Sterzing. The man said nothing. He pointed to a large building down the street, and then turned and continued the march without ceasing his chant.

The hospital proved to be the meeting room of the town hall. The sick and the dying were on litters on the floor. Among them moved a few nuns and priests, and some men whom Theo recognized as barber-surgeons and apothecaries. The cries of the plague victims rang in Theo's ears. The stench of the place was sickening in his nostrils. Theo walked over to one of the men.

"I am a doctor. Let me help you."

The man turned and stared at Theo's ragged clothes. "A doctor? The doctors have all run away! Don't bother me with your crazy talk. There's work to be done here." He bent over a patient.

Theo seized him by the arm. "I tell you I am a doctor! My name is Paracelsus. Surely, you have heard of me?"

At the sound of Theo's voice, one of the other men looked up. With a glad cry, he ran to Theo and embraced him. "Doctor Paracelsus! Oh, Master! It's really you! Don't you remember me? I'm Poschinger — I was a member of your circle at Colmar!"

"Max Poschinger! How good to see you once more!"

"Look, everyone!" called Poschinger. "Sterzing is fortunate. Doctor Paracelsus has come to us! He will help us fight the plague." He turned to Theo. "All the physicians have fled. We don't know what to do. Will you direct our work?"

"Of course!" Theo let his knapsack slide to the floor. His eyes shone. Here was a challenge for Doctor Paracelsus! The other Paracelsus, the mystic, the questioner, disappeared in a flash. "First, we must get this place cleaned up," he said. "Can you get some people to boil water and bring it here? Where can I prepare some medicines? I shall need flasks, retorts, drugs."

"Use my apothecary shop," said one of the men. "I have some alchemical equipment there."

"Good!" Theo bent to examine the patient nearest to him. He looked at the whites of the eyes, the color of the skin. He felt the pulse.

"Aren't you afraid of infecting yourself, Doctor?" asked one of the nurses in a tremulous voice.

Without looking up, Theo answered, "A physician must never fear disease. His only duty is to cure it."

The nun looked down at him with wonder in her eyes. "God bless you for your courage, Doctor Paracelsus!" she murmured.

For four weeks, Theo labored in the pesthouse. The citizens

of Sterzing took courage from his example and helped to care for the sick. Little by little, the Black Death was conquered. One day, there were only ten new cases; the next day, five. Soon the only cases in Sterzing were people who were recovering.

Theo was tired. He took his relaxation in taverns, drinking a glass of cool wine, talking with the common people. With so much religious turmoil going on in Europe, the talk invariably turned to the clash between Protestantism and Catholicism. During these discussions, the other Paracelsus, the mystic, emerged again. He harangued his friends in the taverns for hours, insisting that the breach in the Christan world had to be healed. Like the unity he believed to exist in nature, there had to be a unity in man's thinking about God.

His ideas were not popular with either Protestants or Catholics. People soon forgot about the Black Death in Sterzing. They looked suspiciously at this ragged stranger, who called himself Doctor Paracelsus. One morning, a deputation from the town council came to his door and invited him to leave Sterzing.

Theo smiled bitterly. His only answer was "God is not corruptible, but Man is." As their scowls deepened, he added, "Have no fears. I will go."

To his surprise, his friend Max Poschinger offered to go with him. To have won such a dedicated disciple touched Theo deeply.

Poschinger had many friends in the town of Merano. Here, he had Theo lodged in clean rooms, gave him new clothes to wear, and arranged for him to treat patients again. Theo began to feel more like his old self. Though he spent much time meditating about God and Man and the Universe, he began to write on specific medical subjects. He wrote a description of the plague at Sterzing, and how he had treated the patients in the pesthouse.

Theo had not forgotten his promise to himself to cure miners of their illnesses. He pulled his old notebooks out of his knapsack and sorted them. Putting the notes in order, he wrote his book on the coughing sickness and the metallic poisonings that infected the bodies of the men who worked in the dark hill-tunnels. He described all the symptoms of these diseases carefully, and wrote down the chemical remedies he recommended for their cure. What was more important, he suggested ways of hygienic prevention of the miners' ailments.

Meanwhile, a few words dropped by Poschinger into the proper ears brought some wealthy patients to Theo's door. Those who came away cured spread the glad tidings. Within a few months, there was a steady stream of visitors to Theo's chambers. As his reputation grew, so did his fees. The poisonous slanders of the academic doctors against Theo had not reached Merano. Now he was rich enough to live in style. Dressed in velvet clothing, accompanied by his personal secretary, he rode his own horse proudly to the castles of noblemen who sought his services.

Shining pieces of gold and rich velvet — these were the very things for which Theo had condemned the university physicians. Yet he had to admit that having riches gave a man a comfortable feeling. Besides, he said to himself, I earn my money honestly, not as a quack. My patients go home cured of sickness. My medicines are clean and swift; they are not the dirty greases and plasters of the apothecary shops.

Along with his new-found wealth, the old itch for wandering returned. How different, however, was his journeying now! The fame of Doctor Paracelsus had spread from Merano throughout the adjoining territory. Theo rode from city to city, carefree, happy, welcomed by all. His secretary rode with him. On the way, Theo found time to dictate many letters and treatises.

By the autumn of 1536, he had reached the city of Augsburg with a bulky manuscript that contained everything he knew about the art and practice of surgery. He called it *The Great Book of Surgery*. In it, he condemned the practices of surgeons on the battlefield. He wrote about his concept of the self-healing properties of the human body. The job of the surgeon was to allow Nature to heal wounds in her own way, not to create poisons in a wound.

In Augsburg, Theo found a physician, Doctor Wolfgang Thalhauser, who had been a student with him at Ferrara. Thalhauser was delighted with the book. "You must have this published at once!" he cried. "I have influence in Augsburg. I will write a preface to the book, and publishers will be fighting to print it."

The Great Book of Surgery appeared before the year 1536 had run out. It was a great success. The second printing brought Theo more money than he had ever seen at one time.

But, with the coming of success, Theo's character began to change. He was aware of it, yet he could not help himself. He became quarrelsome and petty. He browbeat his secre-

200

tary, until the poor fellow fled from the house. He argued with his landlord over insignificant expenses. Though people desired his services as a physician, they avoided him socially.

On one occasion, Theo overheard an argument between two men at an inn. One of them shouted invective angrily at the other. The abused man cried, "Don't be so bombastic!" It shocked Theo to realize that his middle name, Bombast, had now become an adjective used to describe an ill-mannered person.

In the summer of 1537, Theo was called to the country of Bohemia, to treat the Grand Marshal of the kingdom, Hohann von der Leipnik. The marshal was old, and he had lived too well. A cerebral hemorrhage had led to acute dropsy and paralysis. There was little Theo could do, except to give the old man laudanum for his pain and to make him as comfortable as possible. Theo moved on to the city of Vienna.

His entry into the city was triumphant. The fact that von der Leipnik had called him added immeasurable prestige to his reputation. Ferdinand the First, King of Bohemia and Hungary, welcomed him to the city. In return, Theo dedicated *The Great Book of Surgery* to him. The king promised to pay for the printing of more of Theo's works. Nothing was too good for the great Doctor Paracelsus.

Theo was in his glory. Here was his chance to take his rightful place in the world of scholars. He assembled all the notes he had made all over the world on magic and superstition. He gathered together the peasant tales about the healing powers of plants and stones. This material formed the basis for a new volume, which he called *The Great Astronomy, or Philosophy of the Macrocosm and Microcosm.*

He also made ready a medical work entitled *On the Tartaric Sicknesses*. This book described his ideas about diseases such as gallstones and bladder stones. Theo used his knowledge of chemistry to point out that such stones were probably mineral salt deposits in the body. "In the joints, as the shoulders," he wrote, "such deposits are very painful. They burn as painfully as Tartarus (the classic name for Hell), therefore I call this substance which is deposited *tartar*."

Theo expected that King Ferdinand would pay for the printing of these books. But somehow the enemies of Doctor Paracelsus caught up with him again. Theo never knew quite how it happened. Suddenly, he was no longer invited to the court. His new friends in Vienna began to snub him.

With his usual ill-timed anger, Theo accused the king of going back on his word. The king's treasurer swore, falsely, that Doctor Paracelsus had been given the money and had squandered it. Theo knew now that the academic physicians had managed to blacken his name at the court. Before he rode out through the gates of Vienna for the last time, he spat on the ground to show his disgust.

Where could he go now? He was forty-four years old and tired. He took a hand mirror from his pocket and stared at it. The face of a stranger stared back. The hairline had receded far back from the forehead, the cheeks were puffy, there were large pouches under the eyes. Theo realized that he himself was ill. Was it the result of working in the mercury mines? Was it the poisonous metals he had experimented with in the laboratory? Was it the years of wandering? He examined his face with a doctor's eye. It was, he decided, the face of a man who did not have many years to live.

What happens in the mind of a man who realizes he does not have long to live? Does he know fear? remorse? sadness? For a brief moment, Theo knew all of these. Then he was overwhelmed by shame and nostalgia. He had been in Switzerland all these years, and had not given a thought to his father, Doctor Wilhelm. What does a dying man do? He goes home, to his family.

When he knocked on the door of the house in Villach, there was no answer. He must be at the school of mines, thought Theo, and turned his steps in that direction. At the school, he heard the incredible news. Doctor Wilhelm had died in 1534, almost four years before Theo's arrival. Johann Schwinger, the alchemist, also had passed away. Doctor Wilhelm's will had been filed at the city hall, the school officials told Theo. They were very kind.

Theo rode slowly to the city hall. He had come too late. Now he was truly alone in the world. The estate of his father — the house, his instruments, his drugs — all was left to Theo. After the necessary papers were signed, he returned to the house. The room in which he and his father used to sit and talk was cloaked in gloom.

Theo hastened to throw open the shutters. Sunlight flooded the room. He looked about him. Nothing had changed! He wandered slowly about the room, touching a remembered table, a book lying open, the comfortable chair before the fireplace.

It was time for peace, Theo decided. He would settle down in Villach to spend the last few years of his life as a respectable practitioner. He would become the man Doctor Wilhelm had been: quiet, useful, respected.

203

Unfortunately, Theo had not reckoned with the reputation of Doctor Paracelsus. When he applied for admission to the medical guild, all the doctors in Villach came out of their homes to stage a demonstration against him. They demanded that the city fathers force Theo to leave at once.

Normally, Theo would have fought the pack tooth and nail. But staring death in the face changes a man. Quietly, with no protest, he sold his father's house and moved to the town of Saint Veith, near the capital city of Carinthia. Many noble and important people called upon him for treatment. Yet his attempts to become a respected, practicing physician were constantly foiled. His enemies were continually slandering his name.

Theo felt it was time to defend himself against the academic physicians of Carinthia. He wrote a little pamphlet which he called *Seven Defences Against My Critics*. In it, he refuted one by one the charges made against him by his enemies.

He petitioned the Carinthian government to print the pamphlet. The council sent him a solemn letter, promising that the manuscript would be printed as soon as possible. The letter was addressed to "the Noble Scholar and Famous Man, Theophrastus Paracelsus, Doctor of Both Medicines" — but the pamphlet never saw the light of day in Theo's lifetime.

One afternoon, a wandering artist knocked on his door. He introduced himself: Augustus Hirschvogel. He had heard of the famous Doctor Paracelsus. It would be an honor to draw the great doctor's portrait. Smiling, Theo consented. The drawing was bold, vigorous, and honest. In profile, Hirschvogel captured the boldness of Theo's look, the defiance in the thrust of his chin.

204

"Is there a motto you would like me to put above this portrait, sir?" asked the artist.

Theo thought for a moment. "Yes, there is an old German peasant saying I like: The man who can do things himself shall be no man's servant."

"That's capital!" said Hirschvogel. "But it ought to be in Latin just for propriety's sake." He thought a moment. "How about this: *Alterius non sit qui suus esse potest.*

Theo nodded approval. Over Hirschvogel's protests, he pressed some gold coins into the young man's hand.

Theo stayed in Klagenfurt, capital of Carinthia, until 1540. He felt his sickness gaining on him. He did not see as many patients as before; riding a horse had become painful. Most of the time, Theo remained in his apartment, writing. He finished an indictment of academic medicine entitled *The Errors of Physicians.* He wrote down new recipes for treating diseases.

Again, one day, Hirschvogel came to his door. He asked permission to draw another portrait. Theo was flattered; he invited the artist in and served him wine and cake. But when he saw the second portrait — a three-quarter profile — Theo shrank back.

"Has the disease progressed so far?" he cried.

The face Hirschvogel had drawn was that of an old man, lined and sagging. The eyes were sad and dulled. It was the picture of a man gazing into the eyes of death.

Theo had been posing with the sword Azoth in his hands. He laid the long sword gently on a couch. "I no longer have any use for you, dear friend," he said.

Hirschvogel was ashamed and apologetic.

"Nonsense, my dear fellow," said Theo. "You drew what you saw. An artist is like a doctor. He must always be honest with himself."

Hirschvogel left. Theo sat staring for a long time into the crackling flames in the fireplace. He remembered his grandmother, standing at the gate of the inn at Einsiedeln, waving good-by, as he and his father clattered their horses over the Devil's Bridge. That had been the beginning of his travels. He had seen more of the world than almost any other man in Europe. What had he really accomplished? What had he learned? Theo closed his eyes. A man's life was in the hands of God. Now, there was nothing left but the desire for peace of mind.

Pressure against him by the medical guild in Klagenfurt increased. But he was saved from further abuse by a call from the Archbishop of Salzburg. The same city from which he had once been forced to flee for his life now recalled him and offered him peace and comfort in his last years. Theo accepted with gratitude.

His illness had advanced more quickly than he had anticipated. Riding to a patient's home was so difficult for him that he only did so when the call came from a very noble or a very sick person. Legends about his miraculous cures persisted. People came from far places to his door every day.

Now, he meditated on matters of God and the spirit, and wrote very little. Doctor Paracelsus was preparing himself for the time when he would meet God face to face.

It was the September of 1541. The nights had begun to grow cooler, hinting of the winter soon to come. Theo sat before the fire in his room, enjoying the warmth of the flames. He had wrapped a blanket about his legs. Suddenly he felt a sharp pain in his head. At the same moment there was a numbness in his left arm. He called for his servant, who slept in the adjoining room. The man came running.

"Call Master Kalbsohr, the notary. You know where he lives — only a few streets away. Tell him to bring pen and legal paper."

Ten minutes later, the servant was back with the notary public. Theo sat quietly erect in his chair. He did not turn his head when they came in.

"Jacob," he ordered, "bring a chair and table and some light for Master Kalbsohr. And be quick about it, I haven't much time!"

The servant ran to do his bidding. The astonished notary

turned to Theo. "But Doctor Paracelsus, this is highly irregular. What —"

"Listen to me, Kalbsohr," interrupted Theo, "I have just had a stroke. Oh, not a bad one. But it tells me of more to come. My moments on earth are numbered. I may die tomorrow, or the next day, or in five minutes — but die I shall, and soon. I want you to take down my will. Jacob can witness it. Are you ready to write?"

The notary nodded.

"Good. *I, Phillip Theophrastus Bombast von Hohenheim, known as Paracelsus, though weak in body, am sound in mind. I commit my soul to God Almighty. May He be merciful to me, miserable creature that I am.* Have you got that?

"*After my death, let three psalms be sung at the Mass. At each singing, let a shilling be given to every poor man who stands before the door of the church.*

"*Let all my surgical and medical goods be distributed equally among the surgeons of Salzburg.* And what is the fee for the execution of a will?"

"Twelve guilders."

"Good. *Let twelve guilders be given to the notary Kalbsohr for the execution of this will. Let ten guilders be given to any existing relatives of mine in Einsiedeln. If any money is left over, let it be distributed among the poor.*"

Theo stared straight ahead into the fire. His lips moved, but Kalbsohr could barely hear the words.

"I don't know what worth my life has been, O Lord. I have been guilty of pride and arrogance and bad temper. But I feel that if I have only left behind a spark, a small spark — perhaps that will touch off a conflagration that will consume

all ignorance and stupidity. I remember in my Latin home-
work at Lavanttal . . . a story about a bird called the Phoe-
nix . . . it never dies, but is consumed by flames and is born
anew. Perhaps medicine will be born anew, because of my
work. I ask no more . . ."

He shook his head. Another pain had come. "Kalbsohr!
Kalbsohr!" he cried.

"What is it, Doctor?"

"In the second drawer of that little desk, you'll find a folded
paper. It contains the epitaph to be engraved on my headstone. Make sure there is enough money for that. And you
can fill in the blanks. Jacob will get you the key."

The notary unlocked the drawer and took out the paper. He
read it through once; then he motioned to Jacob. Theo had
closed his eyes; he seemed to have fallen asleep.

"Listen to this," whispered the notary. He read from the
paper:

HERE LIES BURIED

PHILLIP THEOPHRASTUS

THE FAMOUS DOCTOR OF MEDICINE

WHO CURED WOUNDS, LEPROSY, GOUT, DROPSY

AND OTHER INCURABLE DISEASES OF THE BODY

WITH WONDERFUL KNOWLEDGE

AND WHO GAVE HIS GOODS TO BE DIVIDED AND DISTRIBUTED

AMONG THE POOR.

IN THE YEAR 1541 ON THE ———— DAY OF ————

HE EXCHANGED LIFE FOR DEATH.

TO THE LIVING, PEACE; TO THE ENTOMBED, ETERNAL REST.

Bibliography

The author is particularly indebted to the following works for information about Paracelsus:

Hargrave, John, *The Life and Soul of Paracelsus*. London: V. Gollancz, 1951.

Hartmann, Franz, *Life of Paracelsus*. London: Kegan Paul, no date.

Jacobi, Jolande (ed.), *Paracelsus, Selected Writings*. New York: Pantheon Books, 1951.

Pachter, Henry, *Magic into Science*. New York: Henry Schuman, 1951.

Stillman, John Maxion, *Paracelsus*. Chicago: Open Court, 1920.

Stoddart, Anna M., *The Life of Paracelsus*. London: John Murray, 1911.

Telepncf, Basilio de, *Paracelsus, A Genius Amidst a Troubled World*. St. Gallen: Zollikopfer & Co., 1945.

Waite, Arthur Edward, *The Hermetical and Alchemical Writings of Paracelsus,* 2 vols. London: James Elliott, 1894.

Nova Acta Paracelsica, Vols. 1-5. Basel: Verlag Birkäuser, 1944-1948.

An excellent translation of some of the shorter works of Paracelsus, and one that is most readable, is: Sigerist, Henry (ed.), *Four Treatises of Theophrastus von Hohenheim*. Baltimore: Johns Hopkins Press, 1941.

The following works may also be of interest to the reader: Browning, Robert, *Paracelsus;* Schnitzler, Arthur, *Paracelsus.*

Events in the life of Paracelsus, and some of the legends about him, were used in: Goethe, Johann Wolfgang, *Faust;* Marlowe, Christopher, *The Tragical History of Doctor Faustus.*

Index

213

KOBOLDS, *see* Gnomes

LAUDANUM, 131, 155
Lavanttal, 34-35
Leoniceno, Dr. Niccolo, 83, 85-93, 95, 173
Leprosy, 74-75
Luther, Martin, 81, 149, 177

MAXIMILIAN, Emperor, 10, 75, 83, 93, 96
Mercury, 31, 33, 103, 120, 133, 184, 190-191, 202
Minerals, *see* Ores
Mines, 11, 19; school of, 11, 144; construction of, 13-16; fire damp in, 18, 20

NATURAL PHILOSOPHY, 77, 106, 188

OPORINUS, 168, 173, 174-175, 178, 182, 183, 185-186
Ores, 11-13, 16; roasting of, 14

PARACELSUS, 91; Einsiedeln, 2-8; Villach, 3-4, 10, 13, 14, 82-84, 147-148, 203-204; alchemy, 11, 22-28, 31, 37, 56, 86, 107, 108, 146, 171, 173, 186, 188, 190; Lavanttal, 34-39; Tübingen, 41-63; at medical school, 50-55, 85-93; with wandering scholars, 59-72; Vienna, 75-80, 201, 202; plague, 79-80, 195-198; Italy, 85-109, 133-134; French disease, 92, 102, 147, 182, 183-185, 187; military surgeon, 97-105, 110, 118-121, 141-142; travels in: France, 109, 111-115; Spain, 110, 111; Africa, 110; England, 115; Ireland, 115; Netherlands, 116-117; Hansa cities, 117-118; Denmark, 118; Sweden, 118-119; Poland, 120-123; Russia, 124-132; Egypt, 135-138; Rhodes, 139-142; Salzburg, 148-155; Strassburg, 156-157; Basel, 159-180; Colmar, 181-183; Nuremberg, 183-189; Peasants' War, 149-155; *Treatises on Dropsy, Coughing*

Sickness, and Gout, 163; *On the Diseases That Deprive Man of His Reason,* 163; ideas on mental illness, 163, 191-192; *Three Chapters on the French Disease,* 188; *Paragranum,* 188; *Hospital Book, The,* 189; *Paramirum,* 192; philosophy and mysticism, 193-195; *Surgery, The Great Book of,* 200-201; *Astronomy, The Great,* 201; *Tartaric Sicknesses, On the,* 202; *Seven Defenses Against My Critics,* 204; *Errors of Physicians, The,* 205
Paragranum, 188
Paramirum, 192
Paris, University of, 71, 112
Peasants' War, 149-150
Pharmacy, 110, 119, 143, 146, 167-168
Philosophers' stone, 24-25, 186
Plague, 79-80, 195-198

RUSSIA, 123-125

SALT, 191
Scholars, wandering, 60-72
Seven Defenses Against My Critics, 204
Straw Street, 44-45
Sulfur, 31-33, 190-191
Surgeon, *see* Barber-surgeon
Surgery, The Great Book of, 200-201

Tartaric Sicknesses, On the, 202
Tartars, 127-132
Theology, 81, 106
Tübingen, University of, 41-44, 50-58; oaths at, 44

VADIANUS, *see* Waadt, Joachim von
Vienna, 75-80, 201-202
Villach, 3-4, 10, 13-14, 82-84, 143, 147-148, 203-204

WAADT, JOACHIM VON, 58, 76, 78, 189-190, 193
Wittenberg, University of, 59, 81

214